A selection of the

Best Inns & in the Eastern

GW00670533

Compiled by: Michael Campbell

Edited by: James Lawrence

CONTENTS

Published by
Bracken Publishing
Bracken House, 199a Holt Road
Cromer, Norfolk NR27 9JN

ISBN 1 871614 10 4

Printed by Broadgate Printers, Aylsham, Norfolk.

February 1992

CHAMPION BEER
of
BRITAIN - 1990/91

This is to certify that

Adnams Bitter

was judged to be
CHAMPION
Standard Bitter
of Britain

at the
GREAT BRITISH BEER
FESTIVAL
BRIGHTON, AUGUST 1990

John M. Cryne
National Chairman

From Suffolk's
Oldest Brewery
Britain's Finest Beer

SOLE BAY BREWERY · SOUTHWOLD · SUFFOLK IP18 6JW · TELEPHONE SOUTHWOLD (0502) 722424

Important

Please note:-

1. *Dishes quoted from menus are examples only, and not necessarily available at all times.*

2. *The listing of brewers' beers and lagers does not mean that the full range is necessarily available.*

3. *Prices, where quoted, may alter during the currency of this guide.*

4. *Every effort is made to ensure accuracy, but inevitably circumstances change and errors and omissions may occur. Therefore the publisher cannot accept liability for any consequences arising therefrom.*

5. *This is a selection: it is not claimed that all the best inns and pubs are featured.*

6. *Your comments about any establishment, favourable or not, are particularly welcome. Correspondents who especially impress the editor will receive a complimentary copy of the next edition.*

7. *Special note to publicans: if your house is not included, please do not be offended! The area covered is very large and time limited. If you serve good food in pleasant surrounds, please write and we will visit you.*

FURTHER COPIES OF THIS OR OUR OTHER GUIDES MAY BE OBTAINED BY WRITING TO:–

Bracken Publishing
Bracken House
199a Holt Road
Cromer
Norfolk NR27 9JN

Enclose payment as follows:–

Eastern Counties (Inns & Pubs)	£4.00
Eastern Counties (Hotels & Restaurants)	£3.50
Cotswolds, Thames Valley & Chilterns (Inns & Pubs)	£3.50
Midlands (Inns & Pubs)	£3.50
West Country (Inns & Pubs)	£3.50
South East (Inns & Pubs)	£3.50

Prices include postage and packing.

No order will be accepted without prior payment, other than from book retailers.

THE WOOLPACK INN

Walpole Cross Keys, nr King's Lynn. Tel. (0553) 828327
Location: Off A17, 2 miles east of Sutton Bridge.
Credit cards: Not accepted.
Bitters: Adnams, Broadside, Toby, Tartan.
Lagers: Red Stripe, Carling, Carlsberg.

Examples of bar meals (lunchtime 7 days, evenings Wed – Sun): *Yorkshire puddings with chicken/beef/vegetable stew filling, homemade soup, omelettes, burgers, ploughman's, sandwiches.*
Examples of restaurant meals (lunch & evening, 7 days): *steaks, homecooked ham/beef, chicken curry, haddock, cod, scampi, salads, fruit & nut pilaff, vegetarian goulash. Children's menu. Trad Sun lunch (booking advised).*

The brooding, slightly eerie atmosphere and vast skies of the fens make the area unique, quite unlike anywhere else in the country. Agriculturally it is very rich, and in the 16th century, when the pub was built, wool was transported across the marshland by packhorse – hence the name. Equine paraphernalia is everywhere, and looks well against the cottagey furniture and Yorkstone fireplaces. Pool and darts provide diversion, and every Sunday the old beams shudder a little to the strains of Country & Western, 60's pop or the occasional disco. Barbecues are sometimes held, and a function room is available for private parties. Landlady Margaret welcomes children, and has a garden and playroom. Orchid World and African Violet Centre are in nearby Terrington St Clements.

THE HARE ARMS

Stow Bardolph, nr Downham Market.   Tel. (0366) 382229
- Location: Off A10 between King's Lynn (9 miles) and Downham Market (2 miles).
- Credit cards: Not accepted.
- Bitters: Greene King.
- Lagers: Kronenbourg, Harp.

Examples of bar meals (lunch & evening daily): *homemade pate, curry, lasagne, daily specials e.g. stilton & bacon soup, chicken breast in lemon & prawn sauce, pork steak in brandy & peppercorn sauce, selection of fresh fish.*
Examples of restaurant meals (evenings Mon.– Sat. Booking advised): *basic grills & fish plus chef's special selection e.g. seafood crepe, marinated pigeon breast, monkfish in seafood sauce, pork fillet en croute, venison with redcurrants. Trad. Sun. lunch.*

Pleasantly situated in a small village, this popular ivy clad inn has been recommended by Egon Ronay 10 years running for the delicious wholesome fare, achieving the only star rating for food in Norfolk. Fresh local produce is used whenever possible – crab and lobster in summer, pheasant and game in winter. The high standard restaurant, a beautifully proportioned room, offers a menu of traditional and international dishes changed frequently. The 'Old Coach House' is available for a variety of functions, from private dinner or office parties to weddings (and family use on Sundays). Families are also welcome in the sizeable conservatory or attractive garden. Whatever the occasion, rely on good food and service in this exceptional country pub and restaurant.

5

THE FARMERS ARMS INN & RESTAURANT AT KNIGHTS HILL HOTEL

Knights Hill Village, South Wootton, Kings Lynn.   Tel. (0553) 675566

Location:	On roundabout at intersection of A149 and A148.
Credit cards:	Access, Visa, Diners, Amex.
Accommodation:	8 singles, 34 doubles, 11 twins, 5 masters, all en suite & with full facilities (some non-smoking). £64–£76 single, £74–£86 double. Weekend breaks £50 pp per night, bed & breakfast & £14 meal allowance.
Bitters:	Adnams, Bass, Sam Smiths, Stones, Ruddles, guests.
Lagers:	Carling, Tennents Extra, Tennents LA.

Examples of bar/restaurant meals (all day, every day): *'Farmers Boots' (deep fried potato jackets with delicious filling)*, *'Green Wellies' (same but vegetarian filling)*, *gamekeepers pie, steak hogie, barbecued ribs, char-grills, Norfolk kebab, whole lemon sole, scampi, swordfish, cod, chilli, veg. lasagne, salads, cobs, blackboard specials. Mississippi mud pie, lemon lush pie, death by chocolate, luxury icecreams. Children's menu. Trad. Sun. lunch & full a la carte in hotel.*

Part of a unique 11-acre complex, The Farmers Arms was converted in 1986 from 17th century working farm buildings, its rustic origins being quite unmistakable: flint walls, cobblestone floors, lots of 'snugs' (ideal for children), and a super function room in the old hayloft. The food is good and wholesome, very fair value, and available all day! Country music lovers should go along Wednesday nights. Petanque is played in the garden, and occasional barbecues held. Children's parties and wedding receptions are a speciality, and with a very smart hotel and restaurant on the same site, every conceivable requirement is catered for.

THE KING'S HEAD HOTEL

Great Bircham, nr Kings Lynn.   Tel. (048 523) 265
- Location: B1153, village centre.
- Credit cards: Access, Visa, Amex.
- Accommodation: 2 doubles, 3 twins, all en suite.
- Bitters: Adnams, Bass Charrington.
- Lagers: Carling, Tennents Extra.

Examples of bar meals (lunch & evening, 7 days): *chicken cacciatore, steak & kidney pie, homebaked ham, steaks, curries, crabs, oysters & lobsters in season, salads, sandwiches, specials eg osso bucco, oxtail in red wine.*
Examples of restaurant meals (evenings except Sunday, bookings advised. Lunchtimes by reservation): *halibut Grenobloise, Dover sole meuniere, brodetto (shellfish in garlic butter), steaks, Scottish salmon, scallopine al marsala, pasta specialities. Trad. Sun. lunch.*

The Royal Sandringham Estate, to which the hotel once belonged, draws thousands of visitors to this lovely part of Norfolk. Birdwatchers, yachtsmen and all lovers of gentle, rolling countryside will find spiritual sustenance in unspoilt nature. Sustenance of a more material kind is the speciality of The King's Head, where food is served in all three bars, and in the rather pretty restaurant. The proprietor is Italian, so naturally children are welcome, and have their own room – there's also a large garden (and car park). Historic Kings Lynn and Houghton Hall are very close by, so one is ideally placed for a protracted stay.

THE GIN TRAP INN

High Street, Ringstead, nr Hunstanton.   Tel. (048 525) 264

        Location: Village Centre.
    Credit cards: Not accepted.
         Bitters: Greene King, Charrington, Worthington, Adnams, Toby
                   Gin Trap Own, guests.
         Lagers: Carling, Tennents, Tennents L.A.

Examples of bar meals (lunch & evening, 7 days): *homemade lasagne, homemade steak & kidney pie, Norfolk pie, Narborough trout, mixed grills, vegetarian dishes, scampi, home cooked ham, Danish open sandwiches, steaks, peppered or smoked mackerel, ploughmans, plus daily specials e.g. chicken & ham pie.*

Margaret and Brian Harmes took over this 17th century coaching inn in 1987, and have improved comfort without 'modernising'. Countless gin traps have been cleverly adapted as light fittings, and rural implements of all kinds cover the ceiling. The portions served are both generous and reasonably priced, a fact which has not escaped the locals' attention! There are two car parks, one of which has stocks where miscreants were once pelted. This lovely corner of England is great walking country, and the Gin Trap is a much favoured watering hole amongst ramblers (who are politely requested not to enter with muddy boots, on account of a very expensive monogrammed carpet!). To round off the trip, why not combine your visit with a look at the adjacent country and sporting art gallery. Children permited in walled beer garden. Occasional visits from Morris dancers.

ANCIENT MARINER INN AT LE STRANGE ARMS HOTEL

Golf Course Road, Old Hunstanton.   Tel. (0485) 534411
      Location: Off A149, by lifeboat station.
   Credit cards: Access, Visa, Diners, Amex.
Accommodation: At hotel, 3 singles (from £48), 15 doubles (from £65), 15
           twins, 5 family, all en suite & with full facilities.
           Special breaks & reduced rates for children.
       Bitters: Adnams, Bass, Charrington, guest.
       Lagers: Carling, Tennants Extra, plus speciality beers from around
           the world.

Examples of bar meals (lunch & evening, 7 days): *prawn or tuna hoagie, cod, scampi, barbecued turkey, steaks, chicken tikka, veg lasagne, mariners smokies, filled potato shells, ploughman's, daily specials. Death by chocolate, Dutch apple tart, fresh fruit salad. Children's menu.*
Examples of restaurant meals (as above): *many choices as above, entrecote au poivre, salmon, daily specials. Trad. Sun. roasts in hotel.*

The only east coast resort to face west, the views from Hunstanton on a clear day, across The Wash to Lincolnshire, are quite spectacular. This gracious 17th century country house stands in its own grounds, which sweep right down to the sea. To its rear, 'The Ancient Mariner' captures a little flavour of the 'briney', in part by felicitous use of nets, and an old rowing boat mounted over the bar. There is a separate restaurant with conservatory extension, and an eating area in the bar (divided by a flint wall) which, like the family room, looks out over the garden. Children have swings for recreation, adults tennis courts. Sister pub to The Farmers Arms (South Wootton) and Windmill (Gt Cressingham).

THE LORD NELSON

Burnham Market.   Tel. (0328) 738321
        Location: On Fakenham Road, near village centre.
  Credit Cards: Not accepted.
Accommodation: 1 twin, 1 double, 1 single. S/c cottage in the village.
        Bitters: Ruddles, Websters, Norwich, Woodfordes Wherry.
        Lagers: Holsten Export, Carlsberg, Budweiser.

Examples of bar meals (lunch & evening, 7 days): *homemade soups, mushroom Barrington (stuffed with garlic butter & herbs), Nelson prawns (with grapes in light curry mayonnaise), plaice, scampi, jacket potatoes, daily specials e.g. lobster thermidor pot.* Examples of restaurant meals (lunchtime 7 days, evenings except Sun & Tues): *some dishes as above, crab & samphire soup, marinated fish, local trout with ginger, steaks, fresh fish, oysters, mussels. Homemade cheesecake, ginger meringue. Trad. Sun. lunch (booking advised).*

Fresh, innovative, and with a strong leaning to seafood best describes the food at this very popular inn (far more attractive than first appears from the road), in one of Norfolk's loveliest villages. Quality home cooking has won a place in major guides and the final stages of the Guinness Food Appeal, the latest in a steady succession of awards. Landlord Peter Jordan not only catches his own trout, but is also an expert on wild funghi. The old barn, now a function room, doubles as an art gallery displaying work by, amongst others, landlady Valerie Jordan. Besides a lounge bar (children welcome), there's a public bar with darts and pool, and a charming little restaurant (no smoking) with good, inexpensive wine list. Barbecues are held on the patio in summer. Nelson was born near here, and several hostelries take his name – be sure to get the right one!

THE SANDPIPER INN

55-57 The Street, Wighton, nr Wells. Tel. (0328) 820752
Location: Off B1105.
Credit cards: Not accepted.
Accommodation: 2 twins, 1 double, from £25 (£15 single). Tea & coffee.
Bitters: Sandpiper, Adnams, guests.
Lagers: Red Stripe, Heineken.

Examples of bar meals (lunch & evening, 7 days): *steaks, haddock, plaice, scampi, vegetarian burger, ploughman's, daily specials eg chilli, lasagne, spaghetti Bolognese, steak & kidney pie, tandoori chicken, pizzas.*

The glorious Norfolk coastline has long been a Mecca for birdwatchers, but more and more people are discovering its many other charms. This has resulted in a marked improvement in the standard of food and accommodation, previously quite poor, to meet their needs. Originally The Carpenters Arms, The Sandpiper is a good example. Its origins as early 18th century cottages are unmistakable: a double-sided brick fireplace, rough walls, beamed ceilings and cottage-style furniture, with an interesting collection of plates. Pool and old-fashioned pastimes such as darts and shove ha'penny are there, but tradition yields to occasional Italian or Chinese evenings, for example, and barbecues with disco in summer. Barry and Jean are the innovative licensees; they brought long years of experience here with them in 1984, and have secured a place in a major national good pub guide. They welcome well behaved children (and dogs on leads), and have a large garden. Attractive views over Stiffkey valley. Near Wells-Walsingham railway.

THE CROWN HOTEL

The Buttlands, Wells-next-Sea.   Tel. (0328) 710209
      Location: On tree lined green at rear of town centre.
    Credit cards: Access, Visa, Amex, Diners.
Accommodation: 1 single, 9 doubles, 4 twins, 1 family (10 en suite). New
                 residents' lounge.
      Bitters: Marstons, Adnams, Tetley, John Bull.
      Lagers: Castlemaine, Stella Artois.

Examples of bar meals (lunch & evening, 7 days): *goujons of white fish, seafood tagliatelle, steak & kidney pie, prawn & tomato gougere, grills, omelettes, burgers, salads, sandwiches, ploughmans.*
Examples of restaurant meals (as above): *seafood bouche, smoked sea trout, mushrooms stuffed with chicken pate, lambs kidneys sauted with sherry & cream, roast duck with a sauce of fresh pears & brandy, fresh Scottish salmon poached in dry white wine with green grapes, steaks, Crown mixed grill.*

Proprietors Marian and Wilfred Foyers take the prerequisites of fresh quality ingredients and skilful preparation very seriously, and enjoy an enviable reputation well beyond East Anglia. The menu changes daily and is complemented by a tasteful selection of wines from various regions along with an explanatory map. Children are welcome in certain areas, and dogs permitted. Despite the Georgian facade, the hotel is actually Tudor, and the view from the restaurant is of a lovely green with great mature trees attractively dappling the light. Wells town is quaint and relatively unspoilt, and the beach is superb, backed by quite delightful natural pinewoods.

THE THREE HORSESHOES

Warham, nr Wells-next-Sea.   Tel. (0328) 710547
      Location: Village centre.
    Credit cards: Under review.
Accommodation: 2 singles, 1 double, 1 twin & 1 double en suite, + 2 s/c
                   cottages in N. Creake.
       Bitters: Woodfordes, Greene King, guests.
       Lagers: Carlsberg.

Warham, Norfolk   JanetBeckett

Examples of bar/dining room meals (lunchtime 7 days, evenings except Thurs): *local Stiffkey cockles, pink shrimp snack, Norfolk sausages, salads, sandwiches, daily special. Damson crumble, steamed chocolate sponge, Nelson cake.*

Nowhere in England has time passed more gently than here in Norfolk, and this classic flint village proves the point. Especially, this anachronistic 18th century cottage pub will evoke memories of a less frantic age. The two small bars are totally 'un-modern', to the extent of a 1940s fruit machine in one corner. Bare floors, open fires, old furniture and gas lighting complete the agreeable illusion. A separate building houses a children's room with pool and darts, and an attractive garden borders a stream and the village green. A new dining room has been added, in response to growing demand for fresh seafood at reasonable prices, the house speciality. Also good value is the accommodation, in a picturebook cottage with roses round the door and working water pump in the garden – an idyllic rural retreat.

THE WHITE HORSE HOTEL

4 High Street, Blakeney.　　　　　　　　　　　Tel. (0263) 740574
Location:	Village centre.
Credit cards:	Access, Visa, Amex.
Accommodation:	2 singles, 4 doubles, 1 twin, 2 family, all with full facilities. From £30 pp incl. Special winter midweek breaks.
Bitters:	Adnams, Ruddles, Websters.
Lagers:	Carlsberg, Holsten Export.

Examples of bar meals (lunch & evening, 7 days): *deep fried herring roes on toast, fisherman's pie, sirloin steak, ploughman's, sandwiches, daily specials eg potato & parsnip bake, grilled sardines in garlic butter, lasagne. Spotted dick, treacle tart, bread & butter pudding.*
Examples of restaurant meals (every evening plus Sun. lunch. Booking advised weekends): *seafood mornay au gratin, pork in cider & cream sauce, sirloin steak garni, supreme of chicken bonne femme, vegetarian dish. Summer fruit pudding, veiled peasant girl.*

After 25 years of neglect, this Tudor coaching inn is now quite unrecognisable after total renovation by new owners, to the eminent satisfaction of locals and visitors alike. Blakeney is surely the region's prettiest village, and the views over the quay from some of the very well appointed soundproofed bedrooms are superb. The intimate little restaurant (converted from stables), overlooking the attractive walled courtyard, has already acquired a worthy reputation for good food, accompanied by an excellent wine list. Another worthwhile reason for a visit is the Gallery room, where is displayed an everchanging stock of paintings, prints and sculptures (for sale), and which doubles as a family or function room. Car parking. No dogs.

THE KINGS ARMS

Westgate Street, Blakeney. Tel. (0263) 740341
Location: Near quayside, west end of village.
Credit cards: Access, Grand Met, Visa.
Bitters: Norwich, Webster, Ruddles.
Lagers: Fosters, Carlsberg.

Examples of bar meals (lunch & evening, 7 days. All day Sundays & holidays): *homemade pies, seafood pasta, local crabs, mussels, prawns, salads, vegetarian dishes, daily specials. Evenings only: steaks, fresh cod, local trout, salmon, gammon steaks, scampi, daily specials.*

Blakeney would be many people's choice for East Anglia's most picturesque village. Its flint cottages, alleys and courtyards are a delight on the eye, and the views from the quayside over the marshes provide a lovely backdrop. Just off the quayside, The King's Arms was once three narrow fishermen's cottages, but is now one of the most popular pubs in the area, recommended by national guides. Howard and Marjorie Davies left the world of the Black and White Minstrels and My Fair Lady 19 years ago and took over from the previous landlord who'd reigned for 45 years! They welcome children (who have their own room, and swings in the large garden) and even dogs if the bar is not full (which in summer it usually is). Smokers themselves may appreciate the facility of a no smoking room to enjoy the good food. See if you can spot the 1953 flood tide mark on an inside wall.

THE PHEASANT HOTEL

Weybourne Road, Kelling, nr Holt.   Tel. (0263 70) 382

Location:	On A149 between Blakeney and Sheringham.
Credit cards:	Visa, Mastercard, Eurocard.
Accommodation:	32 doubles/twins/family all with en suite bathrooms. Special disabled facilities. Col. tv's, tea & coff. From £26 pp double, £36 pp single. Winter rates.
Bitters:	Adnams, John Smith. Plus Beamish stout.
Lagers:	Bitburger, Carlsberg.

Examples of bar/restaurant meals (12 – 2pm, 7 – 9pm, 7 days): *garlic mushrooms, steak & kidney pie, lasagne verdi, steaks, chicken chasseur, seafood platter, vegetarian lasagne, crab salad, daily specials. Freshly made pizzas (also take-away). Afternoon tea.*

"The refinement of a manor house at B & B prices!" – this imposing early 19th century house, set amongst pine trees in three acres of ground, does suggest 'expensive', but to the contrary, both food and accommodation are good value. Situated adjacent to Muckleburgh Hill (from where you have the finest views of this Heritage Coastline, designated an area of outstanding natural beauty), it remains one of the last 'undiscovered' corners of England. Just half a mile form the sea, it is one of the country's most renowned birdwatching areas. Well behaved children are welcome, and have an extensive play area (including woodland) in which to romp, plus a large TV indoors. Occasionally special evenings are arranged.

THE JOHN H. STRACEY

Briston, Melton Constable.   Tel. (0263) 860891
      Location: On B1354 towards Aylsham.
Accommodation: B & B.
        Bitters: Sam Smith, Adnams, Burtons, Tetleys, Whitbreads.
        Lagers: Ayingerbrau, Castlemaine, Skol, Carlsberg, Heineken.

Examples of bar meals (lunch & evening, 7 days): *king prawns, homecooked ham, steak & kidney pie (speciality), lasagne, gammon, steaks, scampi, seafood platter, ploughman's.* Examples of restaurant meals (as above): *halibut mascotte, salmon a la Stracey, fillet Mexicaine, chicken Espagnol, duck Normandy, steaks. Trad. Sun. lunch £6.95.*

Named after the former world welterweight boxing champion by a previous admiring landlord, this 16th century inn began as a resting and shoeing place for horses – the old stables are now the restaurant. Those indifferent to sport or history will nevertheless appreciate the home cooked food, served in generous portions – the ham is a favourite, tender and melt-in-the-mouth. For several years now Ray and Hilary Fox have retained a loyal local following, for this is one of the better known pubs in the area. Though on a crossroads, it enjoys a fairly peaceful location overlooking fields, with a small garden (and large car park) to the side. The countryside around here is amongst the best in Norfolk; very near is Stody Hall with its magnificent display of rhododendrons, and Blickling and Felbrigg Halls are also close. Also, the coast is just a few miles away, so an overnight stop may be in order. Children welcome.

THE BOAR INN

Gt Ryburgh, nr Fakenham.   Tel. (032 878) 212
        Location: End of village, opp. 13th century church.
        Credit cards: Access, Visa, Connect.
        Accommodation: 1 double, 2 twins.
        Bitters: Wensum (own brand), Adnams, Sam Smiths, Tolly Cobbold.
        Lagers: Labatts, Carlsberg.

Examples of bar meals (lunch & evening, 7 days): *mushroom royale (cooked with stilton & garlic), spaghetti bolognese, steak & kidney pie, shepherds pie, salads, steaks, curry. Gateaux, fruit crumble, Italian ices.*
Examples of restaurant meals (as above): *smoked salmon, prawn creole, steaks, roast duck with black cherry sauce, rogan josh, rahmschnitzel.*

Very popular locally, so best to book for the restaurant, and as all is cooked to order, allow a little extra time to be served at peak periods. Take the opportunity to look around this ancient inn; the cosy beamed bar is warmed by an open fire in winter, and the dining room is also very attractive and spacious. Or stroll the few yards to a lovely stretch of the clear River Wensum, which meanders through nearby meadows. The patio by the car park is a sun trap, but the pleasant garden, scented with roses, provides cooler shade. All this plus a comprehensive, international menu has regularly secured an entry in more than one national guide. A good place to stay awhile, and perhaps have your hair styled at the salon on the premises!

THE CROWN

Colkirk, nr Fakenham.   Tel. (0328) 862172
- Location: Village centre.
- Credit cards: Access, Visa, Mastercard.
- Bitters: Greene King, Rayments Special.
- Lagers: Harp, Kronenbourg.

Examples of bar meals (lunch & evening, 7 days): *mushrooms in garlic, homemade soups, steaks, deep fried haddock/plaice, fresh fish of the day, gammon, salads, homemade steak & kidney pie, vegetarian dishes, daily specials eg pork & pineapple curry, chilli, vegetable pasta.*

Folk in these parts seem to be unanimous in praise of their local, and it is hard to find fault with such an honest example of the English country pub at its best. The food is fresh and home cooked, the bar and dining room comfortable and pleasant, and the atmosphere congenial. Traditional games like skittles, shove ha'penny, darts and dominoes provide amusement. In winter, warm the extremities with a good hot meal by an open fire, in summer do the same in the sun on the patio or in the beer garden (formerly a bowling green), perhaps with a bottle of wine from a list of over 50. Pat and Rosemary Whitmore are your amicable hosts, well established here over many years.

19

FLAGS FREE HOUSE

Norwich Road, Marsham.   Tel. (0263) 735000
          Location: On A140 Norwich to Cromer road.
       Credit cards: Accesss, Visa.
    Accommodation: 3 doubles, 6 twins, 2 family, all en suite. Tv's, tea & coff.
            Bitters: Woodfordes, Greene King, Adnams, Bass.
            Lagers: Tennents, Tennents Extra, Tennents LA.

Examples of bar meals (lunch & evening, 7 days): *steaks, American style burger, chicken Kiev, king prawns, scampi, vegetarian curry, stir fry jacket potatoes, many daily specials eg trout flambed in Pernod with cream, roast pheasant in pear & white wine sauce, whole skate wing in butter beer sauce, vegetarian loaf with provencal sauce. Fruit pie, fresh cream gateau, banana boat. Carvery Sunday lunch (booking advised).*

With so much gloomy news of pubs closing, it is refreshing to report the opening of a new one, and a very commendable one at that. Andrew Viner and Paul and Jacky Cornwell, an amiable and enthusiastic trio, opened their doors in September 1991, and word of the good food has travelled fast. No expense has been spared in the renovation of this striking white 18th century house: the split level open plan bar is beautifully carpeted and furnished, as are the bedrooms. Work is underway on a beer garden, and a large conservatory is planned! Flags from around the world establish the theme, draped from the beams and illumined over the bar, and tall flag poles stand guard over the car park. Special evenings, like Halloween, are celebrated, and barbecues will be arranged in season. Well-behaved children welcome. Very near Blickling Hall and Marsham Heath bird sanctuary.

AYLSHAM MOTEL & RESTAURANT

Norwich Road, Aylsham. Tel. (0263) 734851
    Location: 10 miles from Norwich towards Cromer (near roundabout).
    Credit cards: Access, Visa, Switch.
Accommodation: 2 doubles, 11 twins, 1 family, all with full facilities.
    Bitters: Adnams, Smith's Sovereign.
    Lagers: Ayingerbrau, Carlsberg.

Examples of bar meals (lunchtime every day): *homemade steak & kidney pie, lasagne, plaice, scampi, steaks, salads, jacket potatoes, ploughman's, toasted sandwiches, daily special eg savoury lamb, poached salmon.*
Examples of restaurant meals (7 days) Lunch: *panfried trout with mussels, roast Norfolk chicken garni, omelettes. Sun. roasts £7.75. Spotted dick, lemon lush pie, sherry trifle.* Dinner: *halibut steak with tomato & garlic sauce, beef stroganoff, steaks, four vegetarian choices.*

Quite unlike any other establishment in these pages, this fairly new addition to the Norfolk scene, though not a pub as such, merits inclusion as a small and friendly family-run hotel, offering good comfortable accommodation and generous portions of fresh, home-prepared food. The Springalls, themselves local people, have in the past two years or so (aided by chef Peter Daniels), won the respect of others. It's ideally placed, being just 15 minutes from Norwich, the Broads, Felbrigg Hall and the coast. Blickling Hall and the Bure Valley Railway are virtually on the doorstep. Up to 120 can be accommodated for private functions, social or business, and there are exceptionally good facilities for the disabled. Well behaved children welcome. Garden and ample parking.

THE CROWN

Banningham, nr Aylsham. Tel. (0263) 733534
- Location: Opposite church.
- Credit cards: Not accepted.
- Bitters: Greene King, Tolly Original & Mild, John Smith, guest.
- Lagers: Hofmeister, Kronenbourg.

Examples of bar meals (lunch & evening every day in Summer, evenings only Wed – Sun from Nov to March): *mushrooms with garlic & stilton, steaks, scampi, plaice, pizza, gammon steak marinated in cider, chicken qtr in wine, jacket potatoes, ploughman's, daily specials eg steak & kidney pie, Devonshire beef casserole, Italian chicken. Meringue special, Norfolk tart, death by chocolate, bread pudding. Trad. Sun roasts from £4.50.*

Definitely not a restaurant! Proprietors David and Elizabeth Scott see good food as crucial, but are equally keen on the informality which is the stamp of a successful pub. Theirs is one of the most popular in the area, and although a room is set aside for eating there's inevitably 'overspill', so one may eat in any of the four pleasant, timbered bar areas, with fresh flowers and warmed by log fires. Exotic national theme evenings, like Italian, Mexican or Indian add colour, but the building itself is rooted firmly in English traditions, 17th century and standing right in the shadow of the church. In a display case is an 1851 bible presented by Rev. Bickersmith, composer of the hymn 'Peace, perfect peace' – appropriate enough in this tranquil little village. There's a family room and garden, and ample parking.

THE WALPOLE ARMS

Itteringham, nr Aylsham.   Tel. (026 387) 258
      Location: Village outskirts.
  Credit cards: Not accepted.
       Bitters: Adnams, Bass, Greene King, guests.
       Lagers: Lowenbrau, Tennents.

Examples of bar meals (lunch & evening, 7 days): *homemade pies (eg steak & mushroom, steak & kidney, chicken & tarragon), steaks, fish pie (in white wine sauce), fresh local trout, vegetarian chilli/lasagne, ploughman's, sandwiches. Trad. Sun. roasts (booking advised).*

Rarely does such an unpromising frontage conceal such a striking interior. Taking its name from our first prime minister (whose family home, Mannington Hall, is very near), this 17th century cottage has been transformed – clever deployment of old timbers, exposed brickwork and an open log fire has created the desired effect. Itteringham is a sleepy hamlet, lost in the romantic North Norfolk countryside, with its leafy lanes and footpaths ideal for ramblers. The river Bure glides lazily past the front of the pub, and a trout farm (open to the public) just yards away provides for the kitchen (all food is homecooked). Families are always welcome, and there is a large, sunny garden. Rated by CAMRA. Close to Blickling Hall and Weavers Way.

ELDERTON LODGE HOTEL

Cromer Road, Thorpe Market.   Tel. (0263) 833547

Location:	Gunton Park, off A149.
Credit cards:	Access, Visa, Amex.
Accommodation:	4 doubles, 3 twins, 1 family, all with tv, tel., tea & coff.
	From £46 per room.
Bitters:	Adnams, Sam Smith's, guest.
Lagers:	Carlsberg, Holsten Export.

Examples of bar meals (lunch & evening, 7 days): *steak & mushroom pie, curry, mixed grill, scampi, roast of the day, daily specials.*

Examples of restaurant meals (as above): *fried squid, chicken Kashmir, shellfish medley poached in cream & herbs, salmon Leonora (in sauce of smoked cheese, basil, wine & cream), wild mushroom steak, duckling Montmerency, rack of lamb. Trad Sun lunch (multi-choice) £11.50.*

Edward VII retreated here for clandestine liaisons with Lilly Langtry. It remains well suited as a sanctuary from the pressures of the world, standing well back from the road in six acres on the edge of huge Gunton Park, across which it affords untrammelled views. Built in 1760 of traditional flint, the hotel was for many years the Dower House and Shooting Lodge to the Estate. Edwardian in style, the house retains the quiet dignity one would expect of such a history, but with the addition of modern comforts such as central heating. Your willing hosts are Sandie and Alistair Cameron, who take pride in offering good value-for-money. One is well placed here for the lovely coast, Broads, Norwich, Blickling and Felbrigg Hall. Children welcome.

THE HILL HOUSE

Happisburgh.   Tel. (0692) 650004
      Location: Next to church, off coast road.
      Credit cards: Access, Visa.
      Accommodation: Self-contained double, en suite.
      Bitters: Woodfordes, Adnams, Greene King, weekly guest.
      Lagers: Hofmeister, Fosters, Kronenbourg.

Examples of bar meals (lunch & evenings 7 days, except Sun. & Mon. evenings Nov – May): *daily specials, lasagne, steak & kidney pie, chilli, local crab, char-grilled burgers, salads, carvery bar in summer.*
Examples of restaurant meals (evenings only 7 days, except Sun & Mon Nov – May): *blanchbait, plaice princess (with prawns, peppercorns & cream sauce), giant crevettes in garlic butter, chicken breast in leek & stilton sauce, steaks with speciality sauces (eg ham, asparagus & cheese). Trad. Sun. lunch.*

This was Conan Doyle's favourite retreat – he wrote 'The Dancing Men' at an upper window overlooking Happisburgh's famous golden sands. It's a remarkable Tudor structure with a priest hole in the restaurant ceiling and original dry rot in the timbers! Sandy and Steve Rayner continue to build on their success, and welcome children – in fact there's a family room, but the very attractive beer garden by the sea is to be preferred if weather permits. Railway buffs might like to inspect the Victorian signal box, intended for a coastal line which never materialised. The public bar has a pool table, and there's a small function room. A very well-liked pub locally, and recommended by national guides.

25

THE SWAN INN

Ingham, nr Stalham.   Tel. (0692) 81099

               Location: Next to church.
      Credit cards: Access, Visa, Amex.
  Accommodation: 3 doubles, 1 twin, 1 family, all en suite & with hair dryer, tv & tea & coffee. From £45 double, £35 single. Midweek breaks £39.50 in autumn.
               Bitters: Adnams, Greene King Abbott, Woodfordes Wherry, Yorkshire, guests.
              Lagers: Tennants, Carlsberg.

Examples of bar meals (lunch & evening, 7 days): *cannelloni, moussaka, potato cheese & leek pie, steak & kidney pie, steaks, burgers, Grandma Batty's king size Yorkshire puddings with variety of fillings, cod, plaice, scampi, jacket potatoes with fillings, vegetable lasagne, tagliatelle Nicoise, cracked wheat & walnut casserole, salads, ploughman's, sandwiches. Sunday roasts. Choice of desserts incl. special icecreams. Blackboard specials. Children's menu.*

If ever there were a measure of the way in which Norfolk pubs have improved in recent years, this is it. A few years ago it was more-or-less derelict and forgotten. The transformation has been quite remarkable, and the 14th century thatched freehouse is now one of the most popular in the area, with the added benefit of five high quality bedrooms, all with four-posters, in a tastefully converted stable block.

The renovations have not ruined the character of the pub (originally part of a priory), quite the reverse. The old beams, flint walls, brick fireplaces, wooden tables and old photos all combine harmoniously to most pleasing effect. Neither could one be better placed for the famous Norfolk Broads, the deserted sandy beaches of this wild and unspoilt coast, and the fine historic city of Norwich, with some of the best shopping in the country – altogether, a marvellous place to escape for a while.

New owners Iain and Michaela Kemp (since July 1991) are from Suffolk, and have extensive experience in the hotel business. They will be pleased to welcome you, and perhaps tell you stories about the knights which haunt the neighbouring church, and the tragic tale of a young lad who lost his life trying to scale the tower. They also have no qualms should you wish to inspect the kitchen, for it is always immaculate. They stock an excellent range of good beers, and the food is wholesome and served in generous helpings.

The pub has a family room with children's toys, and a small patio to the rear. Dogs are permitted on a lead. Parking is no problem.

THE SWAN INN, INGHAM

SUTTON STAITHE HOTEL

Sutton Staithe, nr Stalham. Tel. (0692) 580244

Location: On A149 Stalham by-pass.
Credit cards: Access, Visa, Amex.
Accommodation: 2 singles (from £29), 1 twin, 6 doubles (from £41), 2 family. Some en suite. Special breaks £64 pp two nights.
Bitters: Adnams, Ruddles, Websters.
Lagers: Holsten, Carlsberg.

Examples of bar meals (lunch & evening, 7 days): *steak, ham au gratin, scampi, lasagne, salads, sandwiches, ploughman's. Children's menu.*
Examples of restaurant meals (every evening, plus trad. Sun. roasts): *Norfolk trout, giant prawns in butter & garlic, halibut steak in light creamy cheese sauce, Norfolk duckling in rich orange sauce, fillet steak savora (stuffed with stilton, enhanced with savora), vegetarian Diane.*

As the photo shows, Sutton Staithe, part of the Norfolk Broads, laps almost to the door of this handsome 17th century farmhouse. Such a marvellous location, although a precious asset, does not in itself make a good hotel. That has more to do with the proprietors, in this case Kath and Danny Taylor, who run it as a friendly, family concern. Consequently, many local people are regulars, and will share the bar, garden restaurant or terrace overlooking the river with tourists and boating enthusiasts in summer. Accommodation is of a high standard, and one is well placed for Norwich, the coast and ofcourse all the attractions of the Broads. Children welcome and well-behaved dogs. Good facilities for weddings, conferences etc.

THE FISHERMAN'S RETURN

The Lane, Winterton-on-Sea.   Tel. (0493) 393305/393631
    Location: Near village centre and fine sandy beach.
    Credit cards: Not accepted.
    Accommodation: Three doubles, one single, from £20 pp incl. Rooms are quaint
       with sloping ceilings. Tea & coff. facilities.
    Bitters: Ruddles, Websters, Adnams.
    Lagers: Holsten, Fosters, Carlsberg. Plus James White & Scrumpy
       Jack cider.

Examples of bar meals (lunch & evening 7 days): *Fish pie, Hungarian goulash, mussel & mushroom lasagne, seafood pasta, grilled Dover sole, burgers and steaks (chargrilled), ratatouille with cheese & garlic bread, salads, omelettes, sandwiches, ploughmans, children's specials. Mississippi mud pie, homemade raspberry tart, blackcurrant crumble.*

Converted from 300 year old fishermen's cottages, this is an extremely popular and surprisingly roomy inn. The maritime theme pervades the bars in the form of old photographs and seascapes. In winter the open fires broadcast their warm welcome – the winds off the sea are bracing at times. To the rear a spacious room for families overlooks a patio and garden with swings. There is also a large room for functions, seating 40 or 60 buffet style. This strange and beautiful coast is a marvellous spot to recharge one's spirits, and for a more prolonged stay there are four charming bedrooms, old fashioned but comfortable. All is homecooked to a standard which routinely earns credit from Egon Ronay and other leading guides. Vegetarian dishes have become a speciality. Good choice of at least 20 malt whiskies, 13 wines and champagne. Dart board.

THE RED HERRING

24-25 Havelock Road, Gt Yarmouth.   Tel. (0493) 853384
     Location: Off St Peters Road, near southern part of old wall.
  Credit cards: Not accepted.
      Bitters: Adnams, Woodforde's Wherry, 3 or 4 guests. Adnam's Mild.
      Lagers: Bittburger, Carlsberg. Plus Scrumpy Jack & Theobald's cider.

Examples of bar meals (lunch & evening, 7 days): *homemade steak & kidney pie with beer, pork in cider pie, spicy mince beef pie, chilli, soups, wide range of sausages made to recipes from all over the world, vegetarian dishes.*

One could be in a friend's sitting room, here in this little Victorian oddity (built around 1860) – it's that homely and comfortable; not plush, but cosy and sociable; very "different," one might say. And the name is unusual, too, taken from the product that made Yarmouth a rich town in the Middle Ages. A more recent claim to fame was the hosting of the World Marbles Championship 1990, held just outside the pub, but more routine are impromptu quizzes, bar skittles, pool, shut-the-box, chess, draughts and various dice games. Children are welcome to join in if well-behaved. Audrey and Graham are your amicable hosts; Audrey, a member of the British Institute of Innkeeping, cooks everything herself, and offers the rare opportunity to try exotic sausages from far off lands. Recommended by good beer guides. Parking in street. Near to museums and seafront.

THE NEW ENTERTAINER

80 Pier Plain, Gorleston.

Tel. (0493) 653218
Fax. (0493) 440241

Location: 300 yards from seafront.
Credit cards: Not accepted.
Bitters: Adnams Extra, Eagle, always at least 5 guests beers.

Examples of bar meals (lunchtime, 6 days): *doorstep speciality sandwiches (eg prawn, tuna, bacon, salami, ham, cheese, corned beef), steak & kidney pie, toasties & other snacks according to availability.*

Many of our largest seaside resorts have a smaller, more refined companion town just along the coast (Brighton and Hove, for example). This is the case with Gt Yarmouth and Gorleston. Although very much Victorian in character, Gorleston is in fact mentioned in the Domesday Book, and nearby Burgh Castle is an old Roman fortress. Victoriana is the theme of this London-style pub, built in 1882 – relatively recent in East Anglian terms. Decor is in the Victorian style, with an unusual rounded end, and has been sympathetically modernised in keeping with the original character. Most come, though, for the excellent ales, including Adnams Extra, which have earned a place in the CAMRA guide for the past four years. The range of food is limited, but the infamous 'doorstep' sandwiches will satisfy most appetites. Both food and ale represent good value for money. The pub is not suitable for children, however, as there is no separate room for them. Car parking.

THE FERRY INN

Reedham.   Tel. (0493) 700429
Location: By River Yare, on B1140.
Credit cards: Access, Visa.
Bitters: Woodfordes, Adnams, Youngers.
Lagers: Becks, Tuborg Gold, Carlsberg.

Examples of bar meals (lunch & evening 7 days): *changing seasonal menu using only fresh produce, with meats from local butchers & hand picked fish from Lowestoft market. Chef's daily specials, vegetarian dishes, salads, fresh filled rolls & sandwiches. Children's menu. Italian menu eg lamb & tarragon pie, baked cod fillet Italian style, pizzas, fillet steak on creamy green peppercorn sauce.*

Very few private ferries still operate, and here is the only one left in East Anglia. It has been carrying vehicles of all kinds since the 16th century, and remarkably is still the only crossing point between Norwich and Yarmouth. The inn is therefore guaranteed fame of a kind, but the Archers, who run both it and the ferry, make it worth a call on its own merit. Apart from serving good food in clean and pleasant surrounds, they are considerate hosts, offering to make up a bottle for the baby and providing changing facilities in the ladies washroom, for example. Older children are well accommodated in a large sun lounge overlooking the river. On a sunny day the table and chairs on the bank are a glorious place to sit and watch the various craft plough the waters, including the ferry itself, ofcourse. There are moorings and a launch ramp, and next to the inn a four acre caravan and camping site, and an interesting woodcraft shop.

THE COACH AND HORSES

57 Bethel Street, Norwich.   Tel. (0603) 631337
    Location: 300 yards from market, towards R.C. cathedral.
  Credit cards: Access, Visa, Diners, Amex.
     Bitters: Rayments, Greene King, I.P.A. and Abbot.
     Lagers: Stella Artois, Kronenbourg, Harp.

Examples of bar meals (lunch & evening every day except Sunday): *western style prawns with spicy dip, range of filled jacket potatoes, Coach & Horses ploughman's special, steak & mushroom pie in ale sauce, chicken provencale, steaks, cheese topped fisherman's pie, vegetarian lasagne, 'torpedoes' (larger than average rolls) with assorted fillings.*

One of the very few pubs in the region to remain open all day – a welcome refuge from the bustle of the city. But it's not at all a typical city centre pub, rather a traditional country inn – no juke boxes etc. for those who crave decibels, but a relaxed, informal atmosphere and good wholesome food. The menu is exceptionally varied and interesting, with proprietors Geoff and Mary Slater taking care that only the freshest produce is used. One end of the L-shaped bar could be described as a small museum; fascinating old photographs and paintings adorn the walls, and poignantly displayed is a child's slipper found in the foundations, a 16th century custom meant to bring luck. The Victorian end, as it is called, comprises U-shaped leather conversation seats and appropriate gaslights. This popular hostelry is just a short walk from the market place, behind and to the left of City Hall.

ST ANDREW'S TAVERN

4 St Andrew's Street, Norwich.   Tel. (0603) 614858
          Location: Opposite St Andrew's Hall.
     Credit cards: Not accepted.
          Bitters: Adnams range, 4 guests.
          Lagers: Bitburger, Red Stripe, Heineken.

Examples of bar meals (11:30am – 2:30pm, cold food 5 – 7pm. Open 11am – 11pm
Fri & Sat. Closed Sundays): *chilli, cottage pie, curry, homecooked ham/beef, vegetarian
lasagne, large granary baps (speciality).*

One of England's finest cities, Norwich is blessed with excellent shopping and many
historic buildings. One such is this 16th century former merchant's house, an
eminently suitable retreat after a morning of treading the fascinating old cobbled
streets and alleys. Behind the Georgian frontage is that special Victorian
atmosphere peculiar to town centre pubs. The walls are covered with old trays,
bottles, jugs pictures, signs et al., plus brewing artefacts. Once the home of Rumsey
Wells (clothiers), the ghost of Old Rumsey is said to have floated by on occasion.
The downstairs cellar bar serves as a function room and sees live entertainment on
Tuesdays and Thursdays, while the conservatory dining room is also a faamily area
(leads to large garden). Landlord Colin Keatley can be proud that his tavern won
the CAMRA award as the best in Norwich. No private parking, but a multi-storey
is only 50 yards away.

THE PARSON WOODFORDE

Weston Longville, nr Norwich.   Tel. (0603) 880106
   Location: Just off A1067, opposite church.
  Credit cards: Not accepted.
    Bitters: Woodfordes Wherry, Adnams Southwold & Broadside,
             Boddingtons, Bass.
    Lagers: Tennents Pils, Stella Artois. Plus Murphy's stout.

Examples of bar meals (lunch & evening Mon – Sat, plus trad. Sun. roasts): *homemade pies eg steak & kidney, homemade curries, chilli, seafood platter, steaks, homemade vegetarian casserole, ploughman's, salads.*

Many readers will know of the Parson as the celebrated 18th century diarist, famed for his prodigious feasting and quaffing. For a man of the cloth he had remarkably relaxed views on contraband, to the extent of burying rum in the garden to foil Customs & Excise. He would be well pleased to have the honour of such a notable establishment, just across the road from his parish church, named after him, and would appreciate even more the victuals served there. The L-shaped bar is constructed, in the style of the 16th century, with exposed timbers and open fires. There's a small separate dining room, and to the rear a well equipped function room (for weddings etc). Well behaved children welcome. Rated in national guides, and now in the able hands of John and Mary Fenton.

THE DARBY'S FREEHOUSE

1–2 Elsing Road, Swanton Morley.   Tel. (0362) 637647
>   Location: Village centre.
>   Credit cards: Access, Visa.
>   Accommodation: B & B at farmhouse (£15.50), 4 holiday cottages, bunkhouse,
>   camping/caravan site, from £9.50 incl Eng. b/fast.
>   Bitters: Woodfordes, Adnams, Mild, 4 guests (always 7 real ales).
>   Lagers: Stella Artois, Carlsberg, Carlsberg Export.

Examples of bar meals (lunch & evening, 7 days): *garlic mushrooms, shrimping net, butcher's wedge, fisherman's catch, chef's Beef & Guinness pie, steak, lasagne, salads, daily specials.*
Examples of restaurant meals (lunch & evening, Wed. – Sun. Other times by arrangement): *smoked trout with horseradish, seafood mixed grill, steaks, roast duckling in black cherry, escalope of pork cordon bleu. Trad. Sun lunch £7.95 (booking advised).*

Part of farmer John Carrick's 700 acre estate, Darby's was skilfully converted from two ancient cottages, exposing original brickwork, ship's timbers, and a superb brick fireplace in the dining room. Parties of 150 to be catered for, inside or out, and the Hudson room takes up to 50, with facilities for conferences or wedding receptions. A recently constructed cellar enables sufficient stillage to present a selection of seven real ales in perfect condition. A children's room has a deep well (covered), and they have a new adventure playground in the garden (which also has a barbecue). A 7 acre field is available for activities like car shows, gymkhanas, horse and carriage clubs, caravan rallies etc, supported by full catering facilities. Ideal stop for tourers, cyclists, hikers etc, and of course for anglers and twitchers.

THE KING'S HEAD

Bawburgh, nr Norwich.   Tel. (0603) 744977
    Location: Village centre.
Credit cards: Mastercard.
     Bitters: Marston, Adnams, Wethered, Flowers, plus two guests.
     Lagers: Moose Head, Stella Artois, Heineken.

Examples of bar meals (lunch & evening, 7 days): *homemade pies (speciality), curries, pasta, quiches, steaks, trout, chicken, beef chasseur, French salad stick, daily specials*
Examples of restaurant meals (lunch & evening, Tues. – Sun.): *trad. Sun. roasts (booking advised), variety of steaks, breaded chicken filled with prawn & lobster, chicken in brandy & cream sauce, King's Head giant mixed grill.*

How many other pubs do you know of that have four squash courts and a bowling green? However, you don't have to be sports minded to appreciate The King's Head. It's a fine old country pub in its own right, and has graced this delightful little village, just a few minutes drive from Norwich, since 1602 (licensed in 1800). The bar is divided in two by a fireplace open on both sides, and on the walls are mounted old firearms and gin traps. But it is for good food that most come here, and which has drawn the attention of national guides. All is cooked to order, and success has resulted in landlady Pamela Wimmer adding a 40-seater restaurant extension. She welcomes children, and maintains a nice little sheltered garden which is a real sun trap. The large car park is a necessity, as this is such a popular venue for Norwich people seeking recreation.

THE WINDMILL INN

Water End, Gt Cressingham, twixt Swaffham & Watton.   Tel. (076 06) 232
  Location: Village outskirts, just off A1065.
  Credit cards: Not accepted.
  Bitters: Adnams (inc. Broadside), Greene King IPA, Bass, Norwich, Yorkshire, Sam Smiths, weekly guest.
  Lagers: Carling, Carlsberg, Fosters.

Examples of bar meals (lunch & evening, 7 days): *hot potted shrimps, peasant's platter (quiche), chicken continental, shepherds pie, char-grill steak, pancake rolls (inc. vegetarian), Windmill platter (not for the faint-hearted), king sausages, lasagne, fisherman's platter, Atlantic prawns, scampi, cod, burgers, salads (inc. homecooked ham), ploughman's. Black Forest gateau, deep dish apple pie, knickerbocker glory.*

Being in such a rural location, one wonders where all the customers come from, but clearly to do such a good trade one has to be a cut above the norm. A wide choice of food, reasonably priced, is one reason, accompanied by fine ales and the warmth and bonhomie special to country pubs. This one dates from the 14th century, and the oldest part doubles as a party room (not weekends). Rural artefacts, open fires, wooden settles and amusing old prints set the tone, cosy but never twee. A bright garden room (children welcome) with grapevine provides a pleasant alternative. The vocal refrains of Country & Western can be heard on Tuesdays, Folk on the first and third Wednesday of each month. Pool, darts, skittles and shove ha'penny. Large garden with swings etc. A regular in major guides.

YE OLDE WILLOW HOUSE

2 High Street, Watton.   Tel. (0953) 881181

Location: Opposite Thetford road, just east of town centre.
Credit cards: Access, Visa, Mastercard, Eurocard, Amex.
Accommodation: 3 doubles, 4 twins, all with full facilities. £35 single,
              £45 double, £10 extra per child. Special breaks.
Bitters: Adnams, Greene King IPA, Toby, Worthington.
Lagers: Carling, Carlsberg, Tennants Extra.

Examples of bar/restaurant meals (lunch & evening, 7 days): *tuna fish in bean salad, Italian soups, cannelloni alla caprese, entrecote pizzaiola, breast of chicken rolled & stuffed with garlic, veal in cream & mushroom sauce, fillet of sole bonne femme, scampi alla provinciale, vegetarian dishes, daily specials. Zabaglione, crepe souzettes. Trad Sun roasts.*

If you love Italian cooking then you should not delay a visit to this striking 16th century thatched listed building. Landlord and lady Carlo and Margaret came here only in January '91, having previously owned two Italian restaurants in London. Their menus always make succulent reading, but for an extra treat look out for special dinner evenings, with cabaret. Cromwell was less interested in gastronomic pursuits than catching catholics when he was here; eight priests hid from him in a secret room. A lady ghost is said to appear on occasion, apparently content to spend eternity among superb original timbers, brickwork and inglenooks, unspoilt by modern decibel machines. Children welcome (outdoor games planned). Barbecue. Function room. Large car park. AA and RAC approved.

THE CHEQUERS

Griston Road, Thompson, nr Thetford.   Tel. (095 383) 360
      Location: One mile off A1075.
   Credit cards: Not accepted.
       Bitters: Adnams, Bass, guest.
       Lagers: Carling, Tennents Extra.

Examples of bar meals (lunch & evening, 7 days): *dish of cockles, hot smoked peppered mackerel, steaks, seafood lasagne, smoked ham, homemade steak & kidney pie, mixed grill, steaks, rack of ribs with barbecue sauce, burgers, seafood platter, open sandwiches (speciality), ploughman's, daily special. Chequers special gateau, cheesecake, fruit pie.*

The chocolate box prettiness of this 17th century thatched cottage causes many a foreign tourist to marvel, and it is enhanced by an idyllic setting amongst tall trees. Parts of the inn date from at least the 14th century, and the tiled flooring, exposed brickwork and timber beams are all original and incredibly well preserved – testament to the careful renovation by Bob and Wendy Rourke when they opened here in 1988. The three bars each have their own character, and significantly different ceiling heights – a headache for those who forget! One may eat in any of them, and there's a snug for children. But many choose to enjoy the rural peace in the garden, and the scene when all the hanging baskets are in flower is a joy to behold. On top of all this, The Chequers enjoys a very good reputation for food. Not one to be missed, even though it is a little out of the way.

THE BRIDGE

Castle Street, Thetford.   Tel. (0842) 751161
      Location: On river.
   Credit cards: Access, Visa, Diners, Amex.
Accommodation: 8 doubles (from April '92).
       Bitters: Ruddles, IPA, Websters.
       Lagers: Holsten, Carlsberg, Fosters.

Examples of bar meals (lunch & evening, 7 days): *Bridge busters (French bread filled with steak/sausage/bacon & cheese/veg. sausage), salads, ploughmans's, sandwiches, daily specials eg wing of skate. Homemade desserts (speciality).*
Examples of restaurant meals (as above): *fresh oysters, beef & onion with ale (topped with puff pastry), game pie, chargrilled chicken breast with spicy barbecue sauce, steaks, vegetable moussaka, daily specials (incl. fresh fish). Children's menu. Trad. Sun. roasts (booking advised).*

The conservatory dining area, which currently seats 32, is to be extended in summer '92 to accommodate 60 (available for private parties) – testimony to a popular formula of good, homemade food, with fresh fish always featured and vegetarians never overlooked. Landlady Janet Webb, who acquired this 19th century pub early in 1991, also owns The Old Mill and Rudolf's Nite Spot in Thetford – live entertainment and disco evenings, as well as gastronomic theme evenings, are very much in vogue. Whirring ceiling fans help cool the energetic, and unusual brickwork and cork are also a feature. The friendly staff welcome families, and the garden has a play area. Darts. Large car park. Bedrooms to be added in April '92.

THE CENTRAL FREEHOUSE

Castle Street, Thetford.   Tel. (0842) 751417
Location:	Market place.
Credit cards:	Visa.
Accommodation:	2 singles, 1 double, 1 family.
Bitters:	Adnams, Greene King, Bass, Worthington, 2 guests.
Lagers:	Red Stripe, Harp, Tennents Extra, Carling, low alcohols.

Examples of bar/restaurant meals (lunch & evening, 7 days, restnt closed Mons): *slices of smoked salmon stuffed with crab dressed in white wine & dill sauce, sliced chicken breast lightly fried with queen scallops, tender lamb steaks fried in butter with juniper berries & Grand Marnier, steaks, spiced cashew nut orange & broccoli risotto. Trad. Sun. lunch £3.65.*

Steve and Marion took up the reins here on July 4th (1991), appropriate enough in the town that is the birthplace of Thomas Paine, author of the American constitution (who may well have supped here). Marion, a qualified chef, does all the cooking, and she and extrovert Steve have become very well liked by the locals in such a short time. Their menus are always highly original and exciting, enhanced further on special nights like Mexican, Spanish or Halloween. The Grade II listed building, with its beamed ceilings and brick fireplace, provides a pleasant environment in which to enjoy it. Two old tunnels from the nearby priory to the castle run under the pub. Children have their own lounge, and a patio is planned for the summer of '92. Weddings a speciality. Centre Parc only 2¹/₂ miles.

CROSSWAYS

Ipswich Road, Scole.   Tel. (0379) 740638
      Location: On A140 at Scole crossroads.
      Credit cards: Access, Visa, Diners, Amex.
   Accommodation: 5 rooms (3 en suite), from £30.
      Bitters: Adnams.
      Lagers: Tennents, Warsteiner.

Examples of bar/restaurant meals (lunch & evening, 7 days): *chicken tikka, lamb & apricot pie, mushroom & stilton stroganoff, Singaporean mah mee, gammon steak with wholegrain mustard, steaks (noted).*

Winner of the Egon Ronay Wine Award for the East of England in 1990, recommended by naional good pub guides, this was already one of the most liked and respected inns of the area, with an especially fine reputation for varied and interesting food, augmented by special nights such as Chinese or Halloween, prepared by chef proprietor (for eight years), Peter Black. Steaks are extra good value. A not-unattractive frontage conceals a truly remarkable interior of oak panels and beautifully proportioned rooms, warm and atmospheric – a great place to stay for those who appreciate character. Since the 17th century the inn has been an important halt on this busy route, and former travellers gratefully accepted the home brewed cider once dispensed from here when it was a private house. Children welcome. Huge garden with barbecue. Function room for weddings etc. Large car park.

THE OLD RAM

Tivetshall St Mary.   Tel. (0379) 608228
         Location: On A140 south of Norwich.
   Credit cards: Access, Visa, Switch.
Accommodation: 5 rooms (inc. 2 suites), all en suite. Satellite tv, trouser
                presses, hair dryers, direct phones, tea & coffee.
         Bitters: Adnams, Greene King Abbott, Ruddles County, Websters.
         Lagers: Carlsberg, Holstein, LA.

Examles of bar meals (7:30am – 10pm every day): *homemade steak & kidney pie, moussaka, lasagne, chilli, curry, fresh fish, fruits de mer, steaks & grills, burgers, aubergine & mushroom bake, veg lasagne, salads, rolls. Pina colada gateau, Alabama soft rock pie, American style cheesecake.*

No matter at what time, the car park of this 17th century coaching inn seems always to be quite full – even at four in the afternoon! It is without doubt one of the most popular hostelries in the entire region, with a name that goes well beyond. The reasons are not hard to discern: as well as being open all day from 7:30am, the menu is enormous, and comprised of good, wholesome favourites, served in belt-loosening portions and in an amiable, lively atmosphere. Not surprisingly, then, it features in just about every major national guide, a credit to John Trafford, who has built this enviable success over the past five years. Special occasions are honoured – roses for ladies on Valentine's Night, Beaujolais, Mothering Sunday, Halloween and others. Children welcome. Large garden. No expense has been spared to make the newly added accommodation quite superb.

THE BIRD IN HAND

Church Road, Wreningham.   Tel. (0508) 41438
    Location: Village centre.
    Credit cards: Visa, Amex.
      Bitters: Adnams, Woodfordes, Flowers, Marston's Pedigree, Castle
            Eden, two guests.
      Lagers: Stella Artois, Heineken.

Examples of bar meals (lunch & evening, 7 days): *homemade steak & kidney pie, chicken & mushroom pie, lasagne, curry, scampi, burgers, ratatouille, salads, jacket potatoes, ploughman's.*
Examples of restaurant meals (as above): *steaks & grills, trout with cashew nuts, chicken supreme in port & stilton sauce, surf & turf, salmon steaks, homemade pies, nut roast, cottage cheese & spinach pancakes, salads. Trad. Sun. roasts (booking advised).*

John and Carol Turner arrived here two years ago armed with a training from the British Institute of Innkeeping and high hopes. All expectations have been exceeded, necessitating a staff of 35, including three chefs. To have achieved this in such impecunious times clearly indicates they are doing something right! The large, appetising menus are part of the answer, but the beautiful interior, far surpassing the promise of the exterior, is also quite exceptional. The bar was once a stable, and that special farmhouse ambience is unmistakable; the restaurant is even called The Farmhouse, and is furnished most handsomely. There are occasional jazz nights but always a pianist on Wednesday evenings. Well behaved children welcome, and there's a large garden. Weddings and private parties a speciality. Plans for a large function room and accommodation by 1993. Superb washrooms!

THE COUNTRYMAN INN

Ipswich Road, Tasburgh. Tel. (0508) 470946
     Location: On A140.
     Credit cards: Not accepted.
     Bitters: Adnams, Bass, Greene King, guests.
     Lagers: Carling, Tennents, Tennents Extra, Tennents LA.

Examples of bar meals (lunch & evening, 7 days): *steak & kidney pie, breast of chicken with ham & cheese filling, steak & onion pie, moussaka, omelettes, burgers, ploughman's, daily specials eg curry, lasagne.*
Examples of restaurant meals (evenings only, 7 days – may also be taken in bar): *avocado with prawns, whitebait, veal escalope, char-grilled steak, scampi, plaice. Trad. Sun. lunch.*

The A140 has been the main route between two of the region's principal towns (Norwich and Ipswich) for centuries, and for the last 400 years The Countryman has been a refuge for the weary taveller. But it is also favoured by locals, who come for good, homecooked food, excellent choice of ales and very reasonable prices. The patio and large garden, overlooking rolling fields, provide a sheltered retreat but in unkind weather one will find the two well upholstered bar areas quite amenable. Seating is arranged in semi-circular fashion to aid good conversation, one topic of which might be the unusual collection of stuffed birds. Guests may eat in the bars or small, attractive restaurant. Bill and Sheila Barclay provide the hospitality, and have done so successfully for quite a few years.

THE SWAN MOTEL

Loddon Road, Gillingham, nr Beccles.

Tel. (0502) 712055
Fax. (0502) 711786

Location:	On main road, ¼ mile from Beccles.
Credit cards:	Access, Visa.
Accommodation:	10 doubles, 4 twins, 2 family, 1 executive/honeymoon suite with 4-poster and spa bath. All with full facilities. Special breaks Sept – March.
Bitters:	Adnams, Marston's Pedigree, Bass, McEwans, Tartan, Toby.
Lagers:	Becks, Red Stripe, Carlsberg, Carlsberg Export.

Examples of bar meals (lunch & evening, 7 days): *honey roast chicken, lamb curry, steaks, scampi, cod, plaice, lasagne, cauliflower cheese. Apple crumble, pineapple sponge, banana split.*
Examples of restaurant meals (as above): *grilled halibut/skate with butter & herbs, fresh lobster, steaks, roast loin of pork, homemade chicken Kiev. Trad Sun roasts (booking advised).*

In five acres of gardens and meadows right on the Norfolk/Suffolk border, this family owned, quality country motel sets out to cater for both tourist and business visitor, with the very considerable boon of being open all day from 7am weekdays, 8am weekends (closes 3pm – 6pm Sundays). Norwich, Yarmouth and Lowestoft are all an easy drive, and the Norfolk Broads are right on the doorstep. Built in 1934 on the site of an old pub of the same name, accommodation throughout is of a very high standard and beautifully furnished. The washrooms are positively palatial – you would be hard put to find their equal anywhere. Mitch and Chris are the proud owners: they welcome well-behaved children and have facilities for the disabled. Pool table and darts. Barbecue.

THE PLOUGH

Market Lane, Blundeston, nr Lowestoft. Tel. (0502) 730261
  Location: Just off village centre.
  Credit cards: Not accepted.
  Bitters: Adnams, Ruddles, Websters, Norwich.
  Lagers: Fosters, Carlsberg, Holsten Export.

Examples of bar meals (lunch & evening, 7 days): *homemade soup, breaded mushrooms & dip, lasagne, chilli, tuna pasta bake, scampi, cod, plaice, homemade steak & mushroom pie, steaks, burgers, filled jacket potatoes, vegetarian dishes, salads, ploughman's, daily specials eg chicken Kiev, deep fried camembert. Banana cheesecake, chocolate gateau. Children's menu.*

"Barkis is willing" and he set off from here on his coach in 'David Copperfield'. Letters still arrive from distant places addressed to Dickens' eponymous hero. The great author must have supped here; built in 1701 it was quite well established even in his time. He would surely find it still to his liking. Original oak panelling and exposed beams together with high back settles and open fires combine most agreeably in the large lounge bar. The public bar has old-fashioned skittles, and children are permitted in the small dining room (booking advisable at weekends). The large garden is a sheltered spot, and just a step across the large car park will take you to the Plough's own bowling green. Pat and Linda are the amiable couple who, over seven years, have made this unique pub very well regarded in the area – well worth a visit even if you're not a Dickens fan.

THE CHEQUERS INN

23 Bridge Street, Bungay.   Tel. (0986) 893578

Location: On Ditchingham road, near town centre.
Credit cards: Not accepted.
Bitters: Everchanging selection of seven real ales.
Lagers: Lowenbrau, Carlsberg Export.

Examples of bar meals (lunchtimes Mon – Fri): *homemade curries, casseroles, steak & kidney pie in Beamish stout, steak & onion in ale, lasagne, fresh fish (Weds), jacket potatoes, doorstep sandwiches, salads, ploughman's, vegetarian.*

Proud to be called a real ale house (recommended by good beer guides), Vicky Desborough's 16th century town pub is yet much more than a mere drinkers' den. Food is all homecooked and hearty, the welcome warm (extended to well-behaved children), and the single through lounge most accommodating. The ceiling beams hang with dozens of old jugs, the walls with brasses and other bric-a-brac, and the furniture is cottage style. A covered patio has a barbecue which can also be used for private functions. There's no food served in the evenings, so this is a time to sample some of the excellent ales, brought here from all over the country, in a conversational atmosphere further enlivened by entertainment laid on occasionally. Bungay Castle and the famous Earsham Otter Trust are nearby attractions. Car park.

THE GREEN DRAGON FREEHOUSE & BREWERY

Broad Street, Bungay.   Tel. (0986) 892681
    Location: 150 yards off A143, towards town centre.
  Credit cards: Not accepted.
     Bitters: Chaucer, Bridge Street (both own brews), Adnams, Greene
             King, Wadworth 6X, guests. Guinness & Beamish stout.
      Lagers: Becks, Carlsberg.

Examples of bar meals (lunchtime Mon – Fri, evening Mon – Thurs): *homemade soups (speciality), curries & roti, steak & kidney pie, game pie, hot avocado tartlets, Vietnamese spring rolls, steaks, vegetable ratatouille, wild mushroom pie. Menu ever changing.*

Not the most engaging pub at first sight, but a remarkable one nonetheless. Customers may, if they wish, view the small brewery to the rear, from whence comes the esteemed Chaucer and Bridge Street brews which, together with a range of other excellent ales, makes this a Mecca amongst beer drinkers. But it would be quite wrong to suggest this is just a good 'boozer': food is homecooked and wholesome, the everchanging menu featuring traditional stalwarts alongside the unusual roti (a tasty unleavened bread popular in the West Indies) with curry, for example, plus interesting vegetarian options. Brothers William and Rob have wrought quite a transformation since taking over in April 1991, before which it was rather run-down. Renamed after the house in which Rob used to live (itself a former pub), it comprises of three rooms: a public bar with darts and dominoes etc, the lounge and a small dining cum family room. Small garden with barbecue. Easy parking.

THE BLACK SWAN

Homersfield, nr Harleston.   Tel. (098 686) 204
      Location: Past village green, by River Waveney.
    Credit cards: Access, Visa.
Accommodation: 1 family, 1 double, 1 twin, 1 single. Also Caravan Club
                    certificated location.
       Bitters: Adnams, Ruddles, Websters, guest. Plus Guinness.
       Lagers: Carlsberg, Carlsberg Export, Fosters.

Examples of bar/restaurant meals (lunch & evening, 7 days): *full range from simple bar snacks to 3-course dinner eg beefsteak & kidney pie with suet pastry, cheese & onion pie, beef casserole with horseradish dumplings, chicken & leek pie, pork chops braised in cider. Trad. Sun. roast.*

Step back in time as you stroll into Homersfield over the bridge that has spanned the Waveney for 120 years; a little further and you will find The Black Swan, at the edge of the village green. Since being by-passed, Homersfield (a conservation area) has become a sleepy backwater, immune to the passage of time. The Adair Estate, of which inn and village were once part, has a darker side to its history, one of the marks of which is the four bloody hands on the family arms. The story is told in a framed document over the fireplace in the oak panelled bar. Bill and Jane Ball, son Leighton and daughter Louise (the chefs) are part of a 1,000 year tradition of inn keeping on this spot. They aim, as a family, to suit most tastes and budgets. Having been sympathetically restored over the last six years, the inn offers a choice of four bars, stylish restaurant and games room with pool and darts. The large garden extends to riverside walks through pasture and meadow. Children welcome. Ample parking.

SIR ALFRED MUNNINGS COUNTRY HOTEL

Studio Corner, Mendham, nr Harleston.   Tel. (0379) 852358
      Location: 1¹/₂ miles off A143.
  Credit cards: Eurocard, Visa, Mastercard.
Accommodation: 9 doubles (6 en suite), 1 honeymoon suite. £40 per dbl in
               summer, £30 in winter.
      Bitters: Adnams, Norwich, Courage.
      Lagers: Red Stripe, Carlsberg, Fosters.

Examples of bar meals (lunch & evening, 7 days): *blackboard specials eg cottage pie, lasagne.*
Examples of restaurant meals (evenings Tues – Sat, plus trad Sun lunch): *steak & kidney pie, lasagne, chilli, fisherman's platter, rainbow trout, cod, plaice, steaks, mixed grill, chicken Kiev, salads, vegetarian dishes.*

Taking its name from one of East Anglia's greatest artists, this 16th century freehouse and restaurant stands right on the Norfolk/Suffolk border, in the heart of the Waveney Valley. Not surprisingly, prints of his works (with originals by other artists) form much of the decor in the two bars, two dining rooms and function room (weddings, conferences etc most welcome), all very spacious and comfortable. Each bedroom has a character of its own, well appointed and some with exposed beams. The hotel is suitably placed as a base from which to explore: Norwich, Yarmouth and Lowestoft are not far, neither are the Norfolk Broads, but many come just to fish for trout in the river. Look out for weekly disco and monthly cabaret – pool and darts are always there. Children welcome. Car parking.

THE HUNTSMAN & HOUNDS

Stone Street, Spexhall, nr Halesworth. Tel. (098 681) 341
Location: On A144 Halesworth to Bungay Road.
Credit cards: Mastercard, Visa.
Accommodation: 1 twin, 1 family.
Bitters: Adnams, guests.
Lagers: Red Stripe, Carlsberg.

Examples of bar meals (lunch & evening, 7 days): *steak pie, chicken pie, curry, steaks, fillet of cod in savoury sauce, plaice goujons, veg lasagne, ploughman's, sandwiches, varied specials menu.*
Examples of restaurant meals (evenings only, 7 days): *mixed grill, steak Arizona (fillet stuffed with stilton, wrapped in bacon), prawn curry, trout, lemon sole. Trad. Sun. lunch (booking advised).*

This year (1992) marks the quincentennial of Columbus's rediscovery of America – a turning point in history. Whilst he was so engaged the roof was being put on The Huntsman & Hounds. The sheer size of the oak beams used suggests that the builders fully intended the building to last for at least 500 years, but it is less clear why the ceilings slope so steeply out from the centre. Two inglenooks, back-to-back but no longer sharing the same fire, shed their warmth and light over the bars, reflected in the handsome terra cotta flooring in the Public. Furniture is solid wood and comfortable, and the dining room is compartmented for greater privacy. David and Janet have, over nine years, acquired a reputation for good food in very generous portions. They welcome children and have a garden with duck pond (and new patio). Private dining room for up to eight people, may be used for small conferences. Convenient location for overnight stay.

THE WHITE HART

The Thoroughfare, Halesworth.   Tel. (0986) 873386

       Location: Town centre, at end of main town car park.
   Credit cards: Access, Visa.
        Bitters: Adnams, Benskins, Friary Meux, Greene King IPA, Bass,Tetley.
        Lagers: Lowenbrau, Skol, Castlemaine, Swan Light.

Examples of bar meals (lunch & evening, 7 days except Christmas Day): *homemade pies (eg steak & kidney, steak in ale, chicken & mushroom, gammon & mushroom), casseroles (eg lemon & lime pork, orange lamb, sweet & sour chicken, beef in ale), fresh fish (eg plaice with stilton sauce, cheesy baked cod), lasagne, quiches, salads, ploughman's, sandwiches. Homemade sponge puddings, apple pies, crumbles. Trad Sun roasts.*
NB Open: Mon – Sat 11am – 3pm, 6 – 11pm; Sun 12 – 3pm, 7 – 10:30pm.

Barry and Jenny Howes took over this 17th century town pub only in 1990, after 5 years at The Duke of York, Ditchingham. The reputation which they established there for traditional home cooking, using all local fresh produce, is being firmly maintained. They also undertook complete refurbishment in Marh '91, to make the best of the old beams and inglenooks, and have furnished beautifully in cottage style. They always extend a warm welcome, children included, for whom there are smaller portions and a patio to the rear. Before or after a good meal one could browse through the many quaint and interesting shops in the pleasant pedestrian thoroughfare. Large pay-and-display car park to rear of pub.

THE CRATFIELD POACHER

Bell Green, Cratfield, nr Halesworth.   Tel. (0986) 798206

Location:	15 miles due east of Southwold.
Credit cards:	Not accepted.
Bitters:	Adnams, Greene King, guests.
Lagers:	Red Stripe, Carlsberg, Fosters, Stella Artois.

Examples of bar meals (lunch & evening, 7 days): *macaroni cheese, savoury pancake roll, chicken Kiev, sirloin steak, poacher pie, seafood platter, ploughman's, sandwiches, daily blackboard specials. Homemade desserts.*

As the picture suggests, this is no ordinary pub. The giant octopus was the star of a beach party which, Cratfield being miles from the coast, necessitated the importing of tons of sand! Landlord Graham Barker, who with wife Elaine has served here for 10 frantic years, is blessed with a genius for such bizarre, slightly lunatic but extremely popular stunts. His fertile imagination has been the force behind parachute jumps, scuba diving, windsurfing, raft racing, Christmas in July etc, raising many a laugh and pounds for charity in the process. But there is a more serious side: The Poacher is recommended by leading good beer and pub guides, and food is of a high standard. Some 1700 miniatures, all full, are joined by a collection of jubilee ales, some bottles being over 200 years old. Children are very welcome, and have an excellent play area in the garden.

THE SWAN INN

Fressingfield, nr Eye.   Tel. (0379) 86280
     Location: Village centre, near church, on B1116 (on Norfolk border).
   Credit cards: Not accepted.
      Bitters: Adnams, Courage, John Smith.
      Lagers: Fosters, Hofmeister, Kronenbourg.

Examples of bar meals (lunch & evening, except Sun evening; no hot food Mondays): *steak & kidney pie, trout with almonds, lasagne, steaks, chilli, plaice with prawn & mushroom sauce, Welsh rarebit, salads, ploughman's, sandwiches.*
Examples of restaurant meals (evenings only, Tues – Sat): *homemade shepherd's pie, gammon steak, T-bone steaks. Kiwi & mandarin cheesecake, pineapple caprice, raspberry & apple pie. Trad. Sun. lunch (booking advised).*

This archetypal friendly village local was once three cottages, probably belonging to the church, but the pool room was once that other pillar of the establishment, the bank. Blessed with all the 'olde worlde' trappings (exposed beams, brickwork, horse brasses, inglenook), tradition occasionally takes a back seat for Karaoke and live music nights. Church historians will be interested to know that Archbishop Sancroft of Canterbury was born in the village and was buried in 1693 in the churchyard behind the pub – about the time it was built, so perhaps he supped here. Those whose interests are more temporal will appreciate the large range of traditional homecooked food, best digested with a jar of excellent ale. Alan and Simon Hardy have been pulling pints here for around two years, and welcome children if well-behaved. No garden, but tables to the front.

THE SWAN

Hoxne, nr Eye. Tel. (037 975) 275
Location: Village centre.
Credit Cards: Not accepted.
Bitters: Adnams, Greene King Abbott, Tetleys. Plus mild.
Lagers: Carlsberg, Lowenbrau, Labatt, Swan Lite.

Examples of bar meals (lunch & evening Mon – Fri, plus Sat lunch, plus trad Sun lunch in winter, cold buffet in summer): *homemade soups, haddock & prawn gratinee, pancake mushrooms & cheese, Lancashire hotpot, baked stuffed avocado, sandwiches.* Examples from dining room menu (evenings Wed. – Sat.): *herby brie parcels, roast partridge with braised red cabbage & chestnuts, scampi provencale, lamb cutlets in herby breadcrumbs, vegetarian by request. Rich chocolate pudding with fudge sauce, apple & calvados pancake.*

Time has marched slowly through the village of Hoxne (pronounced 'Hoxon'), and nowhere has it trod more softly than The Swan. Oak floors and beams, huge inglenooks – words bareley do justice to the superb 15th century interior, lovingly preserved by Frances and Tony Thornton-Jones. Once a coaching inn, careful refurbishment has provided a level of comfort which provides an exemplary blend of change without destruction. The honourable tradition regarding food is still observed; good and fresh and at very reasonable prices – from a bowl of soup to a three course meal. There's a games room with pool and shove ha'penny, and a croquet lawn in the garden. Well behaved children welcome. Recommended by national guides.

THE CHERRY TREE

Yaxley, nr Eye.   Tel. (0379) 783462
     Location: Village centre, ¹/₄ mile off A140.
  Credit cards: Not accepted.
       Bitters: Cherry Tree Special Brew, Adnams, Greene King, Double
                   Dragon, Bombadier, guests.
        Lagers: Carlsberg, Carling, Tennents.

Examples of bar/restaurant meals (lunch & evening, 7 days): *deep fried brie, scampi, seafood lasagne, sirloin steak, chicken Kiev, roast of the day, chicken ham & leek pie, cottage pie, steak & kidney pie, game pie, poached hoki, Beryl's batties (speciality), vegetarian dishes, seasonal dishes. Apple pie, treacle pudding, chocolate or toffee bombe.*

"Call in for breakfast!" – the invitation from Tony and Beryl, who open their doors all day (except Sundays). Their 18th century typical country pub is very much the hub of the community hereabouts: 'fun nights' are organised, the quiz team competes regularly, darts and pool are played (in separate bar), Halloween is celebrated and there's live jazz at lunchtime on the last Sunday of each month, but good food and beer merit a visit at any time. An open fire broadcasts its cheer in winter, while a range of 26 malt whiskies will provide inner warmth (there's also a range of eight Australian wines). Children are welcome if well behaved, and the large beer garden has a playground. Yaxley church, Eye Castle and Thornham walks all very close.

THE BLACK HORSE INN & STABLES RESTAURANT

The Street, Thorndon, nr Eye.   Tel. (037 971) 523
Location: 2 miles off A140 Norwich to Ipswich road at Stoke Ash.
Credit cards: Not accepted.
Bitters: Greene King Abbot, Courage Best, John Smiths, guest.
Lagers: Kronenbourg, Fosters.

Examples of bar meals (lunch & evening, 7 days): *steak & kidney pie, lasagne, chilli, pasta shells with cheese & garlic sauce, steaks, mushroom stroganoff, jacket potatoes, ploughman's, salads, sandwiches, daily specials eg sweet & sour chicken, pizza, halibut steak, salmon steak, cottage pie.*
Examples of restaurant meals (lunch & evening, Wednesday – Sunday. Booking advised): *venison casserole with port, poached chicken breast with white wine & hazelnut sauce, rack of lamb, steaks, halibut, salmon, vegetable crumble au gratin. Trad. Sun. roasts. Homemade desserts.*

Local winner of the "Food for the Heart" competition, this 16th century freehouse (run by Rod and Julia Waldron) has one of the most extensive and innovative menus in the area. Everything, from venison or wild boar to sweet-and-sour tagliatelle, is homecooked, and jacket potatoes (with low fat margarine, if requested) are always available as a healthy alternative to fries. The restaurant has been cleverly converted from actual stables, and the stalls are singularly conducive to intimacy and good conversation. In a friendly atmosphere, a warm welcome is extended by the staff, families included. Children like to peer down the 42' well (covered by plate glass!) in the timbered bar, and there's a lawned garden with seating. Occasional Morris dancing and Pony and Trap meets. Beers fresh and well kept.

THE BUCK'S HEAD

Thwaite, nr Eye.   Tel. (0449) 766219

Location: On A140 towards to Diss.
Credit cards: Visa, Diners, Amex.
Bitters: Adnams, Boddingtons, Flowers Best, Trophy.
Lagers: Stella Artois, Heineken.

Examples from lunchtime menu (10:30am–2pm Mon–Sat, 12–2pm Sun): *steaks, grilled skate, halibut, salmon fillet in creamy asparagus sauce, baked stuffed trout, beef bourgignon, curries, country lentil crumble, spinach & mushroom lasagne, salads, pizza, sandwiches, daily special. Trad. Sun. roast (booking advised).*
Examples from evening menu (7–10pm Sun–Thurs, 7pm–11pm Fri & Sat): *steaks, mixed grill, swordfish steak, lamb Shrewsbury, barbary duck breast in honey & lemon sauce, venison in red wine, breaded chicken breast filled with prawns & lobster in seafood sauce, veal a la creme. Many dishes as lunchtime. Divine decadence, banana yoghurt cheesecake, summer pudding.*

Not so much a menu, more a brochure – page after page, offering a choice and variety that can have few equals. Proprietors Steve and Cynthia say that vegetarian dishes are the speciality, but it all makes mouthwatering reading, and prices are most reasonable. This friendly couple extend a warm welcome to their cottagey 15th century pub. Of particular interest in the single beamed bar is the walk-through fireplace, covered in horse brasses. An inglenook takes pride of place in the cosy little restaurant. Well behaved children are permitted, and the large garden (with tables) has a slide. Indoor amusements consist of a pool table and dominoes.

THE CAT & MOUSE

Pages Green, Wetheringsett.   Tel. (0728) 860765
    Location: Take Park Green turn off A140 by TV mast, right at next
                  T-junction, then left and left again.
Credit cards: Not accepted.
     Bitters: Boddingtons, Nethergate, Woodfordes Wherry, Theakstons,
                Pedigree, Flowers, Bass, Castle Eden, Adnams, Brakspear, Tangle-
                foot, Charrington IPA, Fullers London Pride, Batemans XXXB.
      Lagers: Stella Artois, Tennents, Heineken, Warsteiner. Rare ciders.

Examples of bar meals (lunchtimes only, Mon. – Fri.): *homemade soups, lasagne, liver & bacon, beef casserole & dumplings, busters, garlic bread, cheese on toast with mushrooms & bacon, vegetarian dishes.* Evenings: *sandwiches & ploughman's only. Barbecues Fri, Sat, Sun lunch & evening in summer. Special meals available at most times by prior arrangement.*

For rural isolation, you'd have to go a long way to match this delightful little anachronism. In fact, many people do go a long way, for it is quite difficult to find. In 2¹/₂ acres of solitude, the hush is broken only by two donkeys, a pony, five goats, and assorted geese, ducks, hens, rabbits, dogs and cats. Further entertainment is provided by a pool table (plus darts and other traditional games), books and comics scattered round the bar, and often spontaneous jazz and folk music, especially on Thursdays. The bar lounge is charmingly eccentric, with low ceilings, odd furnishings, cat and mouse nick-nacks and bygones. Landlady Anne Booth prepares the food herself (helped by a friend), which may be enjoyed in a quaint little dining room. Husband Roy is proud of the staggering choice of good ales served from new, hygienic state-of-the-art equipment.

THE WHITE HORSE

Badingham, nr Framlingham.   Tel. (0728 75) 280
  Location: On A1120 Stowmarket to Yoxford road.
  Credit Cards: Not accepted.
  Bitters: Adnams, Broadside, draught mild.
  Lagers: Lowenbrau, Castlemaine.

Examples of bar meals (lunch & evening 7 days. Open all day from Whitsun –
September): *homemade pies & quiches, lasagne verdi, steaks, scampi, breaded plaice, chilli,
burgers, vegetarian dishes (speciality), dish of the day. Afternoon teas. Children's menu.*
Examples of restaurant meals (lunch & evening, 7 days): *steaks, duck, venison, fresh
trout, chicken Kiev. Homemade bread pudding, treacle tart, Bakewell tart & more.
Traditional Sunday lunch.*

Alan and Eileen Doughty are Suffolk people, running a handsome 15th century
Suffolk pub. They have introduced all day opening from Whitsun to September, so
you can enjoy afternoon tea with homemade cakes or scones. Menus include
vegetarian options, increasingly a house speciality, and the 30 seater restaurant is
noted for its intimate atmosphere. The two bars, with a collection of rural artefacts
and large inglenooks, are not lacking in character. Neither is the landlady, who is as
warm in her welcome as she is strict about standards – only the best fresh
vegetables, for example. Darts and pool are played inside, while the garden now has
swings, climbing frames, a slide and scramble net. Next door the bowling green
offers more sedate pleasures. Featured in leading national pub guides.

THE CROWN AT WESTLETON

Westleton, Saxmundham.
Tel. (072 873) 777
Fax (072 873) 239

Location: Village centre.
Credit cards: Access, Amex, Diners, Visa.
Accommodation: 17 doubles, 2 singles, private facilities in all. AA 2★ 72%
Bitters: Adnams, Greene King, Sam Smiths, Bombadier.
Lagers: Carlsberg, Tuborg Gold. Plus James White cider.

Examples of bar meals (lunchtimes only 7 days, not Christmas or Boxing day): *poached, fried or grilled fish of the day, steak & kidney pie, Crown mixed grill, smoked mackerel. Homemade treacle pudding, redcurrant & apple pudding. Children's menu.* Examples of restaurant meals (evenings only 7 days, not Christmas or Boxing day): *chicken coronation, stag & boar pie, maigret of duck, baked seafood surprise, steaks, 'Jewels' menu (seasonal) fish soup, quails eggs, braised pheasant in red wine, stir fried beef & scampi.*

Suffolk's 'Best Kept Village' is a title often won by Westleton; the 14th century church is beautifully thatched, and there's a village green with duck pond. Photographs of bygone years on the walls of the inn show very little change, but Rosemary and Richard Price can offer 'state of the art' amenities: six 'Honeymoon' rooms, some with four posters or half tester beds, all equipped with superb bathrooms complete with jacuzzi! The picturesque newly terraced garden (by Blooms of Bressingham) has weekend barbecues, and a very large new conservatory is for the use of non smokers. Inside has an open log fire which spits and crackles on a cold day. Very fresh local fish is the house speciality, skilfully prepared. World famous Minsmere Nature Reserve is just a few minutes walk.

THE BELL HOTEL

High Street, Saxmundham.

Tel. (0728) 602331
Fax. (0728) 833105

Location: Town centre.
Credit cards: Access, Visa, Diners, Amex.
Accommodation: 3 singles (from £25), 3 doubles, 6 twins (£50), 2 family. Most en suite, tv's, tea & coffee, telephone. Weekend breaks £62.50 pp (dinner, b & b).
Bitters: Greene King, Rayments, Scotch.
Lagers: Becks, McEwans, Henry Funck.

Examples of bar meals (lunch & evening, 7 days – bar open all day): *homemade steak & kidney pie, pizzas, steaks, curry, gammon, plaice, scampi, salads, omelettes.* Examples of restaurant meals (as above): Italian:– *fillet steak Napotetana, veal escalopes with marsala, sole fillets in white wine sauce with scampi & tomato sauce, king prawns in garlic butter, pasta dishes, pizzas. Trad. Sun. roasts (booking advised).*

This dignified former coaching inn has been at the centre of life in Saxmundham for over 300 years, and is now sister hotel to the White Horse in Leiston, since its acquisition by John and Jean Doyle. Gourmets with a taste for the Mediterranean will delight at the strong Italian emphasis in both menu and wine list, but there are ample alternatives for those whose preference is for staple English fare. Chef Brian Craven is interested in all types of cuisine, and with wife Sheila he also manages. The hotel is well suited to business or pleasure, and facilities are good for both – a baby listening service, for example, and a fully equipped conference room (weddings also catered for). Children welcome. Car park.

THE WHITE HORSE HOTEL

Station Road, Leiston.
Tel. (0728) 830694
Fax (0728) 833105

Location: On main road into Leiston.
Credit cards: Access, Visa, Diners, Amex.
Accommodation: 4 singles (£33.50), 5 doubles, 4 twins (£52.50), 1 family. Most en suite, tv's, tea & coffee, telephone. 'Let's Go' weekend break £62.50 (dinner, b & b).
Bitters: Greene King, Theakston's Old Peculier, McEwans Export, Exhibition, Scotch.
Lagers: Becks, Kronenbourg, McEwans, Harp.

Examples of bar meals (lunch & evening, 7 days): *ragout of venison, sweet & sour chicken, steak & kidney pie, seafood pancake, trout, smoked haddock prawns & mushrooms tagliatelle, jacket potatoes, salads, ploughman's, daily specials eg steak, cauliflower & brie pie, roast pork. Ipswich almond pudding, real sherry trifle.*
Examples of restaurant meals (as above): *halibut in vermouth sauce, king prawn tails in sweet & sour sauce, steaks & grills, game pie, strips of veal in white wine & cream sauce, chicken breast flamed with Calvados. Trad. Sun. roasts (booking advised).*

Far more attractive inside than out, this 18th century hostelry is exceptionally well equipped: the astonishing play area in the garden will impress even the most hard-to-please youngster, and their parents will appreciate the two bars, restaurant and well appointed bedrooms. Food is of a high order, but special mention must be made of the 100+ illustrated wine list. This wild and beautiful coast is in some ways best seen in winter – John and Jean Doyle offer special Christmas and winter packages, which are very popular. Parking for 16 cars.

THE PARROT AND PUNCHBOWL

Aldringham, nr Leiston.   Tel. (0728) 830221
       Location: Crossroads B1122/B1353.
   Credit cards: Access, Visa.
        Bitters: Flowers, Wethereds, Whitbread.
        Lagers: Stella Artois, Heineken.

Examples from lunch menu (7 days): *local grilled fish, Atlantic prawns, Suffolk smokies (smoked haddock), lasagne, chilli, Sunday roast (Oct–May).*
Examples from evening menu (7 days): *T-bone steak, lamb cutlets Aldringham, fillet steak and king prawn kebabs, roast local duck, pasta dishes, nightly specials.*

The name Parrot and Punchbowl Inn is unusual and of uncertain origin, but back in 1597 'The Case is Altered' was its first, enigmatic name. The exposed beams and superb split level interior bear witness to its great age. Of more historic interest, perhaps, is the association with smuggling in the 17th century. Over the past three years it has been transformed into one of the most successful pubs on this beautiful coast, on the strength of the excellence of the cooking. Children are welcome, and when the weather is clement the enormous garden is at their disposal to burn off energy on the playthings. The garden is also the source of herbs used in the kitchen, and experts will no doubt enjoy identifying them. Complete your visit with a step across the road to the craft centre opposite. Ample car parking.

THE OLD CHEQUERS

Aldeburgh Road, Friston, nr Saxmundham.   Tel. (0728) 88270

Location:	2 miles from Snape Maltings, twixt Saxmundham and Aldeburgh.
Credit cards:	Not accepted.
Bitters:	Adnams, 2 guests.
Lagers:	Carlsberg, Carlsberg Export, Bitburger

Examples of hot lunchtime buffet: *beef & beer casserole, baked Aldeburgh cod with prawns & cheese, stuffed pheasant with apricots & redcurrants, cannelloni verdi ricotta, plus roast ribs of beef on Sundays.*
Examples of evening meals (Mon–Sat): *soused herrings with sour cream, roasted monkfish with tandoori spices, steaks, supreme of chicken with fresh truffles. Belgian chocolate biscuit cake, upside down ginger pudding, butterscotch fudge cake, sticky toffee pudding, creme brulee.*

"THE CHEF IN YOUR KITCHEN", David and Sally Grimwood, have their own food company and delicatessen. They still do most of the cooking, and the many fans from their time at The White Horse at Easton will know that some of the specialities are local fresh fish and game, prepared with verve and imagination. They even organise shooting parties, raising the prospect of downing a bird to be consumed later, perhaps, at their tables! The pub itself is very much farmhouse style, full of pine furniture (including a Welsh dresser where delicacies are displayed for sale), exposed brickwork, beams and a large inglenook. Bar billiards and other time-honoured games are played. Children welcome in walled garden. Recommended by major good pub guides. Very good wine list offers plenty of New World Wines – plus a few surprises!

THE FALCON INN

Earl Soham, nr Framlingham.   Tel. (0728) 685263
          Location: Village centre
      Credit cards: Not accepted.
    Accommodation: 4 rooms, BTB approved. £17.50 p.p. incl.
           Bitters: Adnams, Wethereds, Whitbread.
            Lagers: Stella Artois, Heineken.

Examples of bar meals (lunch & evening, 7 days. Limited menu Sunday lunchtime, due to popularity of 3 course lunch at £6.50 approx): *steak & kidney pie (featured in local paper), home cooked gammon, curries, ploughmans, vegetarian choices.*
Examples of restaurant meals (evenings only, Mon. – Sat.): *venison in red wine, rump steak (noted), duck a l'orange, trout in garlic butter, boeuf bourgignon, chicken Kiev, vegetarian choices.*

England is noted for country pubs and good breakfasts, and you get both in good measure at this well preserved 15th century free house. The traditional friendly country pub atmosphere is fostered by Paul and Lavina Algar and staff, and enhanced by an open log fire in winter. In summer the large garden is a sunny spot for lunch, and children are welcome any time in the pleasant restaurant, with crisp linen and flowers on every table. From the smart bedrooms you can gaze out over a bowling green and the open fields of Earl Soham, winner of the "Best kept Village" award, and well placed to tour Framlingham Castle, the many beautiful churches in the area, and a nearby animal sanctuary. Indeed, if you are touring further afield, this being the heart East Anglia, Sandringham is only 1 1/2 hours, and Constable Country just one hour. Functions catered for. Coaches by apointment.

THE QUEEN'S HEAD

Brandeston, nr Woodbridge.   Tel. (0728) 685307
    Location: Off B1120 from Earl Soham.
    Credit cards: Not accepted.
    Accommodation: 2 doubles, 1 family. £14 – £17 pp incl.
    Bitters: Adnams, John Smiths.
    Lagers: Red Stripe, Castlemaine, Carling. Plus James White cider.

Examples of bar meals (lunch & evening, except Sun evening): *prawn cocktail, smoked mackerel pate, beef & veg. soup, vegetable samosas, meat or veg. lasagne, sausage & onion pie, chilli, beef or veg, burgers, scampi, chunky plaice, chicken Kiev, chicken cordon bleu, local sausages, mushroom & nut pancake, salads, sandwiches. Children's menu. Carvery Saturday evenings (bookings only). Trad. Sun. roasts.*

Recently acquired by Tony and Doreen Smith (formerly of The White Lion, Lower Ufford), this is one of the best known pubs in the area, and has collected many awards, plus accolades from national guides. Among recent ones is Adnam's award for the best kept garden. If the weather precludes enjoyment of this large garden (with play area), the cosy interior of the 400-year-old inn will not disappoint. Dogs are permittted on leads in the rear bar. One is well placed here to visit local attractions, and as well as its own bedrooms the pub has a caravan site to the rear. Children welcome.

THE LION INN

Main Road, Little Glemham, nr Woodbridge. Tel. (0728) 746505
Location: On A12 between Woodbridge and Saxmundham.
Credit cards: Access, Mastercard, Switch.
Accommodation: 2 doubles, 1 single, with full facilities (from spring '92).
Bitters: Adnams, Theakstons, Websters, guests.
Lagers: Carlsberg, McEwans.

Examples of bar/restaurant meals (lunch & evening, 7 days): *homemade soup, steaks & grills, all-day breakfast, Mull of Kintyre scampi, homemade pies, curry, chilli, homecooked ham, trout, veg lasagne, egg curry, mushroom & nut fettucini, jacket potatoes, salads, ploughman's, baps. Homemade chunky apple pie, spotted dick, treacle roly poly, cherry pavlova, chocolate & orange surprise. Children's menu. 3-course trad. Sun. roasts £6.40 (booking advised).*

The lonely blasted beaches, eerily silent estuaries and oozing marshlands of this 'Heritage Coast' are balm to a troubled soul, but the body still requires sustenance, and that is the forte of Peter and Pauline Fry. Pauline and her two colleagues have done all the cooking over the past four years, furthering a tradition of hospitality on this site which stretches back to Domesday. The grade II listed building is graced by exposed timbers (some taken from a 16th century boat), brick fireplace, wrought iron ballustrading, cottagey furnishings and paintings by a local artist (for sale). Pool, skittles, darts and other traditional games are played, and extra fun is to be had on Harvest Supper, Halloween and other nights, plus occasional barbecues in summer. Well behaved children are welcome, and the garden has an aviary and rabbits. Small private parties catered for.

THE CHEQUERS INN

Kettleburgh, nr Framlingham.   Tel. (0728) 723760
Location: Easton to Earl Soham road, about 3 miles from Framlingham.
Credit cards: Access, Visa, Diners.
Bitters: Marstons, Tolly Cobbold.
Lagers: Labatt, Hansa.

Examples of meals (lunch & evening, 7 days): *fresh baked bread, homemade pate, scampi, Hereford chicken, venison pie, steak & kidney pie, fresh fish, Kettleburgh ploughmans. Traditional Sunday roast. Lemon souffle, Queen of puddings. Children's menu.*

Keith and Judith Wilson both have 25 years experience in the business, but came here in December '88 and found this graceful Edwardian building sadly neglected. They have instigated many improvements, not least the wholesome home cooked food from a very wide blackboard choice, served with ebullient good cheer. The bar is a most interesting room, with terracotta flooring and illuminated by huge bay windows overlooking a quiet country lane. The centrepiece is an antique grandfather clock, and it's nice to see an old piano in the corner. Darts and crib are further diversions. A separate dining room seats 24. A good fire is set in winter, or in kinder weather stroll in 2¹/2 acres of garden down to the river Deben. Children welcome.

THE ADMIRAL'S HEAD

Sandy Lane, Little Bealings, nr Woodbridge. Tel. (0473) 625912
Fax (0473) 622299

Location: From Ipswich, turn left off old A12 just before Police HQ.
Credit cards: Access, Visa.
Bitters: Bealings own brand, Adnams, Flowers, Courage, John Smiths, weekly guest.
Lagers: Stella Artois, Heineken, Kronenbourg, Fosters.

Examples of bar meals (lunch & evening, 7 days): *hot & cold buffets, hot smoked mackerel with orange sauce, bouillabaise, grilled skate with lemon & herb butter, beef stroganoff, chicken Kiev, rack of lamb, roast duck, minute steak chasseur. Bread & butter pudding, meringue chantilly, death by chocolate. Trad. Sun. roasts.*

Nelson is the admiral concerned, and the story goes that he met here with Lady Hamilton on occasion. The frontage style is contemporary of that period, but the fine interior preceded him by 200 years. Of special interest is an old well in the lovely little dining room to the rear (available for small private functions), from which water was drawn until about eight years ago. But perhaps the most favoured area in which to sit is the gallery, partitioned by an old timber lattice, although the two pleasant sun terraces are to be preferred, perhaps, in summer. Whenever you visit, expect good food, beer and fair prices. Consequently the pub is very well known locally, but newcomers may have to search a little for this tiny hamlet. Children welcome.

THE KING'S HEAD

Orford, nr Woodbridge. Tel. (0394) 450271
> Location: Village centre, next to church.
> Credit cards: Diners.
> Accommodation: 4 doubles, 1 twin, 1 family, with tv & tea & coff. £19 pp per night. Special winter breaks.
> Bitters: Adnams Bitter, Broadside, Old, & Mild.
> Lagers: Carling.

Examples of bar meals (lunch & evening, 7 days): *monkfish & lobster souffle, fresh local lobster, scallops in sherry & mushroom sauce, homemade fish pie, cod, king-sized prawns in garlic sauce, sirloin steak, crabs, mussels, lemon sole etc in season.*
Examples of restaurant meals (evenings except Sun. & Thurs.): *many dishes as above, fillet steak & oysters, fillets of cod stuffed with scallops, local duckling in lemon & ginger sauce, lobster thermidor, local specialities when available eg bass, mullet, salmon trout, Dover sole, skate.* NB open all day Bank Hols and Saturdays in high season.

Orford is famed for its oysters, and seafood predominates at this celebrated 13th century smugglers inn, personally run by the Shaw family (currently Alistair and Joy) for over 24 years. Alistair derives great pleasure from his individual and creative preparations, as do his customers, including some well known faces, who return again and again, and all the major guides have little but praise. It seems an old lady keeps coming back, too, in spectral form! Children are welcome in dining room or small garden. If you have the foresight to book a room, you could enjoy a superb breakfast in bed (optional) of grilled lemon sole or ham, then a stroll around this delightful village.

THE JOLLY SAILOR

Quay Street, Orford.   Tel. (0394) 450243
          Location: 300 yards from quay.
   Credit cards: Not accepted.
Accommodation: 2 doubles, 1 twin. £30 per room.
         Bitters: Adnams.
         Lagers: Skol.

Examples of bar meals (lunch & evening, 7 days): *fresh Orford cod, steaks, seafood, scampi, pies, smoked mackerel, ploughman's, sandwiches. Trad. roast most Sundays.*

This looks very much a quayside inn, as indeed it was until the sea retreated in the 18th century. But it's only a short walk to get the benefit of the beautiful vista across the river Ore to Orford Ness and Havergate Island, famed for its colony of avocets. A short walk in the other direction will take you to the old castle keep, and the exquisite little village. Having thus stimulated the appetite, repair to this 16th century smugglers' inn, warm yourself by the log fire and sample some of the fare which has kept The Jolly Sailor in national good pub guides for a number of years. Ancient credentials are established by stone flag floors and exposed beams, and strange stuffed Chinese muff-dogs in a case, the origins of which are uncertain. Live dogs are permitted in the public bar only, but there are two other bars and a dining room. Live music sometimes on Saturday nights. Large garden for children.

THE RAMSHOLT ARMS

Ramsholt, nr Woodbridge.   Tel. (0394) 411229
Location: Off Woodbridge-Bawdsey road.
Credit cards: Access, Visa, Diners, Amex.
Accommodation: Two doubles £25 p.p.(Oct–May only).
Bitters: Adnams, guest.
Lagers: Red Stripe, Carlsberg. Also good selection of fine wines.

Examples of bar meals (lunch & evening, 7 days. Extended hours in summer:
Lunch: *cold carvery in summer, salads, fresh fish, hot food in winter, homecooked daily
specials & bar menu. Evening: large choice of starters,steaks, swordfish, lamb cutlets,
mixed grill, 'ship to shore'.*

No photograph can really do justice to the superb vista from the terrace or bar. On a
wide sweep of the river Deben, the views in both directions are breathtaking. The
inn stands at the end of a long country lane, so there's no roar of traffic to disturb
the tranquility. You can enjoy this all day in summer, taking advantage of extended
opening hours, and there's often a barbecue on the go. If poor weather drives you
inside, you'll find two bars and a dining room (the Colonel's room), and an
informal, relaxed atmosphere. Occasionally there's live music. Built around 1747 as
a ferryman's cottage, it's bedrooms have been refurbished to a high standard –
royalty has slept here. It's a great spot for a winter break, especially for birdwatchers,
and though not easy to find, the management will reward you with a "We've
managed to find Ramsholt Arms" car sticker! Recommended by national guides. If
coming by water, contact harbour master George Collins (on the quay) for mooring.

THE MAYBUSH INN

Waldringfield, nr Woodbridge.   Tel. (047 366) 215
       Location: Riverside, at end of village.
   Credit Cards: Not accepted.
       Bitters: Tolly Cobbold.
       Lagers: Labatt's, Hansa Export, Hansa, Tennents LA.

Examples of lunchtime meals (7 days, not Christmas or Boxing day): *home cooked meats, 'ploughpersons' lunch, peeled cold water prawns, pork & egg pie, cod & haddock fillets, dish of the day.*
Examples of evening meals (as above): *some dishes as lunchtime, plus breaded chicken breast stuffed with cream cheese & mushrooms, chicken Kiev, golden seafood assortment, shell-on prawns.*

No doubt about it, The Maybush enjoys one of the most spectular locations of any pub in the region, on the shores of the wide river Deben. The 150 seater garden reaches down to the water's edge, and affords breathtaking views in both directions – reason enough for a visit but, almost as a bonus, the pub itself is first rate. The large bar overlooks the river, so you can feast your eyes whilst treating your taste buds to traditional, wholesome food in a cheering, hospitable environment. A popular family pub, the car park is often well filled, and customers travel from afar; there's no passing traffic, for The Maybush is at the end of a long narrow country lane, very pleasant for a stroll.

THE SHIP

Gun Hill, Levington, nr Ipswich. Tel. (0473) 659573

Location:	Next to church.
Credit Cards:	Not accepted.
Bitters:	Tolly Cobbold, Old Strong Winter Warmer. Mild, Guinness & Original.
Lagers:	Labatts.

Examples of bar meals (lunch Mon. – Sat. – revised daily. Limited Sunday menu – mostly ploughman's.): *smoked roasted ham, pork sausages (with onion, apple & mustard sauce), fisherman's pie, salmon fishcakes, smoked haddock & prawn kedgeree, kippers, chicken leg stuffed with bacon & walnuts, Moroccan meatballs in tomato & basil sauce, nut roast with mushroom & mustard sauce, cheesy vegetable crumble. Spotted Dick, Belgian apple flan, toffee apple tart, treacle tart.*

Drivers hurtling to and from Felixstowe don't know what they're missing. Not far from the A45 is to be found quite beautiful countryside, surprisingly hilly and thickly wooded. In this haven, only minutes from Ipswich and in sight of the river Orwell, The Ship is a little gem – a 14th century smugglers inn, with ancient wood benches and settles, log fires and authentic nautical oddities around the three bar areas. Beer is drawn the old fashioned way, straight from the barrel. Shirley and Bill Waite became the new owners only in November '91, but have over 30 years experience in the trade, and are well known in the area. Their imaginative menus suggest that this exceptional pub is not one to be passed by.

77

BUTT AND OYSTER

Pin Mill, Chelmondiston, nr Ipswich.   Tel. (0473) 780764
     Location: Off B1456 Shotley Road.
  Credit Cards: Not accepted.
      Bitters: Tolly Cobbold – on handpump or from barrel, from the reborn brewery across the river.
      Lagers: Hansa, Hansa Export.
Extended Hours: Winter: Mon–Sat 11am–3pm, 7pm–11pm. Sun 12 noon–3pm, 7pm–10:30pm. Summer: Mon–Sat 11am–11pm. Sunday as winter.

Examples of bar meals (lunch & evening, 7 days): *fishermans pie, smoked chicken with onion & chive dip, savoury sausage pie, pork duck orange & walnut pie, steak & kidney pie, giant prawns, seafood platter, crispy curry pancakes, veal cordon bleu, farm manager's lunch, ravioli. Limited menus summer afternoons.*

Views of the River Orwell as this pub has are a major asset. However, not content to rest on nature's laurels, Dick and Brenda Mainwaring really work at keeping the Butt and Oyster authentic with no intention of trivialising it. The concept works, as national guides and newspapers testify. The locals also treasure it, and the elders will confirm that it is unchanged over 60 years. Even the pub games, some almost forgotten elswhere, live on here; juke boxes and the like do not. The view from the bar and dining room overlooks the boats and river, and at very high tides the river nearly overlooks them. There's an old smoke room with bare floorboards and smoke-stained ceiling. The homecooked food varies daily and is of generous proportions. A children's room is also available, or sit at tables by the river's edge.

THE COMPASSES INN

Ipswich Road, Holbrook.   Tel. (0473) 328332
Location: On main road.
Credit cards: Access, Visa, Diners, Amex.
Bitters: Tolly Cobbold.
Lagers: Hansa Export.

Examples of bar meals (lunch & evening, 7 days): *chicken Kiev, beef stroganoff, cottage pie, salads, ploughmans, lasagne, seafood lasagne, steak & mushroom pie, cod in batter, vegetarian dishes.*
Examples of restaurant meals (7 days): *melon platter, ham & leek tartlet, pasta quills, king prawns with garlic butter, gammon & peaches, steaks, duck a l'orange, poached salmon in bearnaise sauce, beef stroganoff, pork Normandy, chicken on horseback. Trad Sun lunch.*

It is not known when The Compasses Inn was built, its history is uncertain. Travellers once hired ponies here for the journey to Ipswich, which was a safer mode of transport than by boat on the River Orwell, to judge from the engraved ships' timbers dredged up and put on display. Also on display, hanging from the beams, are more than 1000 key fobs. The Victorian restaurant has an airy light atmosphere, a product of the high vaulted ceilings and great tall windows. However, what really makes the Compasses so popular are the generous portions at very reasonable prices. The bar is on a split level with an eating area where children are allowed – they also have a play area overlooked by the restaurant. The more mature can relax in the garden or on the patio with a pint and a good meal. Deservedly features in national guides.

THE BEAGLE

Old Hadleigh Road, Sproughton, Ipswich.   Tel. (0473) 86455
      Location: Cul de sac next to new road, near Post House Hotel.
  Credit cards: Access, Visa.
       Bitters: Adnams, Greene King, Theakstons, Mauldons, guests.
       Lagers: Becks, Kronenbourg, Carlsberg, Dansk LA.

Examples of bar meals (lunchtime only every day except Sunday): *homemade soup, pate, parma ham with melon, local smoked kippers, liver & sausage casserole, cheese & vegetable pie, steak & kidney pie, chilli, ploughmans, farmers lunch, prawns, duck breast, sirloin, chicken & ham pie. Coffee & brandy gateau, cherry crumble.*

Painstakingly converted from four cottages just a few years ago, The Beagle is now a firm local favourite, and quickly won a placed in Egon Ronay's guide. To become so well established so quickly indicates a lot of imagination and hard work. The interior confirms this; two superb inglenooks take pride of place among the exposed beams and the whole is most pleasing, as the usually quite full car park will testify (fortunately, there's ample parking). There is no children's room as such, but there is an extension in the shape of a conservatory onto the lounge where children over five are permitted. The garden is ofcourse still there for sunnier days. William and Nicola Freeth, who have made all the above possible, extend a warm welcome and cordially invite you to try their delicious homecooked fare.

THE ANGEL INN

Stoke by Nayland, nr Colchester.   Tel. (0206) 263245

Location:	Village centre.
Credit cards:	Access, Amex, Diners, Visa.
Accommodation:	6 doubles, all en suite.
Bitters:	Adnams, Greene King.
Lagers:	Carlsberg, Kronenbourg.

Examples of bar meals (lunch & evening, 7 days): *griddled fresh fillet of grouper fish, baby artichokes in vinaigrette, fresh lobster, smoked fillets of trout, vegetable bake, medley of salads, saute of chicken livers with wine mushrooms & herbs. Large choice of blackboard specials changed twice daily.*

Examples of restaurant meals (evenings except Sunday & Monday): *homemade terrine of venison, poached comice pear with fresh scallops, quenelles of chicken with wild mushrooms, brochette of seafood, supreme of guinea fowl, vegetarian dish, speciality fresh griddled fish.*

Although the Georgian facade is pretty enough, it is but a prelude to the very splendid 17th century interior. Looking for the most outstanding feature, one would settle on the gallery which leads from the tastefully refurbished bedrooms to a view over the restaurant. A charming little lounge divides the bars from the two dining rooms, one of which has an ancient 40' well. The restaurant and pub are regularly feted by national guides (including Egon Ronay) for the sheer excellence of the food, which has made The Angel widely admired in the region. The village is a very pretty one, and just 15 minutes drive from Colchester.

THE ROSE INN

Thorington Street, nr Stoke-by-Nayland.   Tel. (0206 37) 243
Location: Dedham Vale.
Credit cards: Not accepted.
Accommodation: 1 double, 1 twin, £25 per room.
Bitters: Adnams, Green King, Rayments, Webster, Kings.
Lagers: Carlsberg, Carlsberg Export, Fosters, Range of bottled.

Examples of bar meals (lunch & evening, 7 days): *porterhouse steaks, curries, steak & kidney pie, half chicken, lasagne, spaghetti Bolognese, chicken Kiev, shepherd's pie, gammon, seafood platter, scampi, cod, salads, ploughman's, sandwiches. Children's meals. Desserts. Trad. Sun roasts (booking advised).*

The rose is the symbol of the Tudors, to which period this fine old hostelry belongs (built 1550). There's no doubting the authenticity of the abundant exposed timbers and brick fireplace, decorated by farming tools, brasses and old horse attire from the local Suffolk Punch stud. The results are most congenial, the atmosphere immediately relaxing. Newcomers Dave and Jean Redding offer a convivial welcome (children included), and take pride in serving good food and ale at modest prices (accommodation, too, is very reasonable). For extra sparkle, they organise regular events, such as musical nights, parties, darts matches and so on. Barbecues in the large beer garden are planned for summer, when the lovely countryside hereabouts is at its best – take the chance to visit nearby Flatford Mill, made famous by John Constable. Ample parking.

THE BELL INN

The Street, Kersey.   Tel. (0473) 823229
     Location: Village centre.
  Credit cards: Access, Visa, Diners, Amex, Luncheon vouchers.
Accommodation: 6 en suite doubles planned for late '92 (this is also a restricted
                  Caravan Club registered site).
      Bitters: From a selection of 35 rotating ales, plus draught Murphy.
      Lagers: Lowenbrau, Carlsberg, Castlemaine.

Examples of bar meals (lunch & evening, 7 days): *braised beef in red wine, savoury sausage plait, chef's own steak & kidney pie, veal cordon bleu, 12ozs & 20ozs T-bone steaks, Cromer crab, Suffolk ham, daily fish special, prawns, genuine ploughman's.* Examples of restaurant meals (lunch & evening every day except Sunday. Trad. roast on Sun. 11:30am – 2pm): *surf & turf (fillet with prawns & crab), lamb Catherine, duck Jamaican, Dover sole meuniere, baked poussin, trout en papillote, tournedos Rossini, vegetarian dishes. Afternoon cream teas all year. Multi-lingual menu.*

"The prettiest village in the world" – a bold claim, but one to which many would subscribe. The Bell, once a coaching inn, has shared the last 700 years with Kersey, and ofcourse is said to be haunted. One can understand a spirit not wishing to leave, for it's an extremely handsome building, inside and out. The double restaurant is full of atmosphere, as are the heavily beamed front and back bars. Proud proprietors Alex and Lynne Coote came here in summer '89, and their home cooking and bonhomie have kept a place in major guides. Families welcome, and sunny patio and garden to rear. Parties well catered for. Les Routiers listed and approved.

SPECIAL OFFER: Present this book on arrival for 10% off a 2-course meal and coffee (Mon – Fri only). Valid in both bar and restaurant.

THE PEACOCK INN

The Street, Chelsworth.   Tel. (0449) 740758

Location:	Village centre.
Credit cards:	Not accepted.
Accommodation:	3 doubles, 1 twin, 1 single.
Bitters:	Mauldons, Greene King, Adnams.
Lagers:	Carlsberg, Kronenbourg.

Examples of lunchtime buffet (every day): *rough game pate, cold meats, smoked mackerel, lasagne, steak & mushroom pie.*
Examples of evening meals (every day): *seafood pasta, grilled salmon cutlet, half duck with orange sauce, homemade quiche, cod, scampi. Mississippi mud pie, hot cherry & almond pudding.*

There's nothing quite like an open spit roast to set the taste buds alight. That's just one enticement to this very special inn which have made it one of the most celebrated in Suffolk. Chelsworth is an exquisite little village of thatched houses clustered along a river bank, and The Peacock has been at its heart since 1470. It has all that one could hope for in the better kind of English country pub: old oak beams, magnificent inglenooks and warm hospitality. In summer, it is a pure delight to sit in the garden and partake of the excellent lunchtime buffet; in winter, its a bowl of hot soup and ofcourse the spit roast. Friday nights sees the venerable old joint jumping to the syncopated ryhthmns of live jazz. Five well appointed bedrooms mean that you can enjoy it all again the next day!

THE CROWN HOTEL

104 High Street, Bildeston.   Tel. (0449) 740510
      Location: Village centre.
    Credit cards: Access, Visa.
Accommodation: 15 rooms (1 with 4-poster), most en suite & with tv's.
       Bitters: Adnams, Mauldon's Black Adder, Marston's Pedigree,
             Nethergate.
       Lagers: Carlsberg, Castlemaine, Warsteiner.

Examples of bar meals (lunch & evening, 7 days): *steak sandwich, eggs piperade, scampi, omelettes, ploughman's, sandwiches.*
Examples of restaurant meals (as above): *crisp vegetables in herby tomato sauce with potato gnocchi dumplings, poached chicken pieces tossed with lightly curried yoghurt mayonnaise, rounds of pork fillet coated in peanuts (fried & served with mango & ginger sauce), steaks, homemade game pie, beef stew with parsley dumplings, fresh fish of day. Trad. Sun. roasts (booking advised).*

Once known as the 'most haunted public house in Britain', this eye-catching 15th century former merchant's house and coaching inn is far from spooky. Over the past few years it has been carefully restored to its former glory, and the splendid interior fully realises the promise of the striking timbered frontage: leaded lights, huge inglenooks, superbly furnished bedrooms, cosy bar and restaurant. Cuisine is of a standard to match, yet prices most affordable. The large secluded garden has also benefitted from care and attention, and makes a very pleasant spot to sit and take the country air – for this is a lovely part of the county, well placed as a base from which to explore. Darts and crib in public bar. Well behaved children welcome. Large car park.

THE TROWEL & HAMMER

Mill Road, Cotton, nr Stowmarket.   Tel. (0449) 781234
    Location: Village outskirts (near Bacton).
    Credit cards: Not accepted.
        Bitters: Adnams, Greene King, Whitbread.
        Lagers: Stella Artois, Heineken.

Examples of bar meals (lunch & evening, 7 days): *kleftiko, moussaka, steaks, kebabs, scampi, salads, sandwiches, ploughman's.*
Examples of restaurant meals (as above): *succulent scotch & local steaks cooked to your satisfaction, mixed grill, tournedos Rossini, steak Diane, East Anglian trout, Dover sole, king prawn in garlic butter, half duck in cherry brandy sauce. Trad. Sun. lunch £11 (3 courses + coffee. Appetising salads of fresh local vegetables. Last food orders 10:30pm weekdays, 10pm Sundays.*

On the front cover of one of our previous editions, this 'Pub of the Year' (as elected two years running by readers of a well known local newspaper) could never be described as commonplace. Even in this area, so well endowed with beautiful buildings, it is exceptionally handsome and enticing. Few others can boast an outdoor pool in large colourful gardens, an invaluable asset in the long hot summers we've had recently. The water doesn't look quite so inviting in January, ofcourse, but there are plenty of other reasons for coming here.
Inside fully lives up to the promise of the exterior. At the end of the L-shaped bar is a superb floodlit inglenook, making its own special contribution to a warm, comfortable atmosphere. There's also the indoor pool – the kind you play on a flat table – in the games room. The 40 seater oak beamed restaurant, tastefully decorated, offers outstanding fresh food at very reasonable prices. One of the favourites, for which diners travel miles, is the mouthwatering 'kleftiko', a 1¹/2lb piece of lamb cooked for six hours until falling off the bone, tender and succulent, and amazing value at £5.50 (at time of writing), including chips and salad.
Partners George and Chris are most amicable hosts, who have brought their Greek origins to bear fruitfully here in the heart of Suffolk. Naturally, everything on the menu is prepared in the kitchen, including humous and taramosalata, but it would not be accurate to identify this as a Greek restaurant, as there are to be found many international and traditional English dishes also.
First time visitors are invited to ring for directions before leaving home.

TROWEL & HAMMER, COTTON

THE FOUR HORSESHOES

Wickham Road, Thornham Magna, nr Eye. Tel. (037 971) 777

Location:	400 yards off A140.
Credit cards:	Access, Visa, Diners, Amex.
Accommodation:	5 doubles, 1 twin, 2 singles, all en suite.
Bitters:	Adnams, Ruddles, Websters, weekly guests.
Lagers:	Holsten, Fosters, Carlsberg.

Examples of bar meals (lunch & evening, 7 days): *fisherman's hotpot, homemade pies (eg chicken ham & mushroom, apricot & walnut), country grill, vegetable & nut cutlets, salads, ploughman's, sandwiches, daily specials. Shoes' special banana split.*
Examples of restaurant meals (lunch & evening, 7 days): *grilled cod with stilton cheese, well hung steaks, guinea fowl forestiere, fresh lobster & other specialities to order, vegetarian choice. Many desserts. Trad. Sun. lunch (booking advised).*

Bar   Restaurant

The Four Horseshoes
Country Inn and Hotel

One of the best known inns in East Anglia, 'The Shoes' is always lively and bustling. As the pictures suggest, it is the archetypal dream thatched cottage, a delight on the eye inside and out. The massive low beams and mud and daub walls suggest great age – over 800 years, in fact. It is the kind of place that has visitors from North America and Australasia wide eyed. The natives are less easily impressed by antiquity; they come more for the abundance of good food from a wide choice, both in bar and restaurant. The current management, which took over only in summer 1990, have had the good sense not to tamper too much with what was already a successful formula.

The bedrooms are luxurious, and residents have their own lounge. Dogs are permitted by arrangement (not in restaurant or bar), and well behaved children are welcome – cots are provided for the very young. This is a lovely area to explore: nearby Thornham Park is full of wild deer and rare orchids, ideal for a quiet stroll. There's a well known herb garden in the village, and Thornham Parva church is worth seeing for its uncommon medieval wall paintings and thatched roof. One is also well placed to travel further afield: north to Norwich and the Broads, east to the coast, south to Ipswich and Constable Country, and west to Bury St Edmunds, Newmarket and Cambridge.

THE GARDENERS ARMS

Church Road, Tostock, nr Bury St. Edmunds.   Tel. (0359) 70460
    Location: End of village green.
    Credit Cards: Not accepted.
    Bitters: Greene King.
    Lagers: Harp, Kronenbourg.

Examples of bar meals (lunchtime only, every day except Sunday): *grills, salads, ploughmans, wholemeal granary rolls, daily specials e.g. curries, fish pie, steak & kidney pie. Snacks in the evening.*
Examples of restaurant meals (evenings only, not Monday or Tuesday): *ratatouille with peanut & cheese topping, poached salmon steak, Gardener's grill, grilled trout, sirloin steak, blackboard specials e.g. fresh brill, duck breast in ginger sauce.*

The name is apt, for the garden really is very pretty, and has been enhanced recently by the addition of a patio. For around 600 years this friendly local has stood on the edge of the green, an eyecatching building in a pleasant village. It is not let down by its interior; a magnificent fireplace occupies almost the entire length of the lounge wall, and combined with tables and chairs clustered round it, and low timbers, the effect is very cosy. The neat little dining area has only four tables, so booking is advisable. The public bar is not short of character either, and has traditional games and a pool table. Reg and Mary Ransome are your genial hosts, and Mary's cooking has merited regular praise from national guides, So don't thrash past on the A45 – pull in for a true taste of Suffolk.

THE FOX

The Street, Pakenham, nr Bury St Edmunds. Tel. (0359) 30347
   Location: Village centre.
Credit cards: Access, Visa.
     Bitters: Greene King.
      Lagers: Harp, Kronenbourg.

Examples of bar meals (lunchtime & evening, 7 days): *chicken tagliatelle, canneloni, seafood tortelli, curries, Pakenham pie, steak & kidney in Abbot ale. Children's menu.* Examples of restaurant meals (every evening, plus trad. Sun. lunch): *steaks, mixed grill, gammon, many various vegetarian dishes.*

It may surprise you that this is seemingly the only village in Europe with both a watermill and windmill – one for 'trivia' fans. It is also distinguished by this well liked country pub, acquired only in July 1990 by Ron and Val Fitch. Ron, who originates from Suffolk, won the 1983 Norwich Brewery Year Award, but it is Valerie who does all the cooking. The partly beamed bar, split by an open brick fireplace, feels very '19th century', but more remarkable is the reading room restaurant, with a unique, peaceful atmosphere, attributable to the fact that it was indeed once a reading room. Darts, pool and dominoes are played inside, while in the very pleasant garden, bordered by a stream with ducks, is a pets' corner, where rare sheep, pigmy goat, donkey, peacocks, bantams, dwarf rabbits and guinea pigs all dwell! Barbecues are held on the patio, often in conjunction with live country and western music. Children welcome and dogs on leads.

THE BLUE BOAR INN

The Street, Walsham-le-Willows.   Tel. (0359) 258889
     Location: Off A143 Bury St Edmunds to Diss road.
  Credit cards: Access, Visa.
      Bitters: Adnams, Theakstons, guest.
      Lagers: McEwans, Carling, Tennents Extra, Red Stripe.

Examples of bar meals (lunch & evening, 7 days): *steak & kidney pie, lamb curry, lasagne, chicken satay, gammon, scampi, plaice, catch of the day (selection of fresh fish), ploughman's, sandwiches.*
Examples of restaurant meals (as above): *Dover sole 'Blue Boar', grilled halibut, swordfish Espagnol, fresh lobster, chicken Kiev, steak Diane, saute of pork Jamaican, escalope of veal marsala. Hazel's hazard, treacle tarts, fruit crumbles. Trad. Sun. roasts.*

Every bit as pretty as it sounds, Walsham-le-Willows is a small village of large, sturdy houses scattered amongst even sturdier old trees. One would hope to find a good traditional country pub at its heart, and one would not be disappointed. Believed to date from the mid-16th century, The Blue Boar may have taken its name from the house of York or the earls of Oxford – both sported the motif. These days it is the sport of horse racing which is celebrated – new licensees (since Sept. 1991) Peter and Jane Tate also own a racehorse, and momentos of the turf are prolific. They have even re-named the cosy restaurant 'Silks and Saddles', but seafood seems to be the forte, fresh from the trawlers' nets. Children are permitted if dining, but if not the large garden is well equipped with playthings (and barbecue).

JUDE'S FERRY

West Row, Mildenhall.   Tel. (0638) 712277
Location: On right-hand-side from RAF Mildenhall (approx. 3 miles).
Credit cards: Not accepted.
Accommodation: 2 twins (1 suited to family use), £15 pp. Tv's, tea & coff.
Bitters: Adnams, Greene King, Worthington.
Lagers: Kronenbourg, Carling, Harp, Carlsberg, Warsteiner.

Examples of bar meals (lunch & evening, 7 days): *homemade steak & kidney pie, steaks, lasagne, gammon, shepherd's pie, mixed grill, chicken Kiev, pork chop, burgers, trout, cod, plaice, scampi, king prawns, salads, veg. lasagne, ploughman's. Trad. Sun. roasts (booking advised).*

The River Lark once lapped right up to the front door of this unpretentious Victorian pub, and people were baptised in the waters. One could easily imagine that Noah's Ark found landfall here, looking at the menagerie in the garden: two donkeys, two pigs, two Shetland ponies, three goats, calves, geese, peacocks, rabbits, ducks, chickens etc.! Children love it, ofcourse, but there's plenty for adults, too – Halloween, weekend disco, karaoke and Cockney nights, for example, plus all the traditional pub games (including pool). The garden is illuminated on summer nights and, complete with bales of hay, provides a fine backdrop for live music. There's also a large brick barbecue, kept going all day if numbers justify. Roy and Olive Newby lay on a warm greeting, and Olive does much of the cooking herself. Weddings and other functions catered for. Slipway and 400' moorings on river.

THE MASON'S ARMS

14 Whiting Street, Bury St Edmunds.   Tel. (0284) 753955
Location: Town centre.
Credit cards: Not accepted.
Bitters: Greene King.
Lagers: Kronenbourg, Harp.

Examples of bar meals (lunch & evening, 7 days): *roast beef, lasagne, chilli, toad in the hole, scampi, plaice, cod, tagliatelle with garlic onions & cream, Yorkshire specials, cauliflower cheese, Chinese spring rolls, vegetable curry, salads, ploughman's, sandwiches, jacket potatoes, daily specials eg Japanese prawns, fresh lobster, crab, mussels.*

Stately Bury St Edmunds has many fine buildings gracing its elegant streets, but it cannot be generally said to be well endowed with good pubs. Happily, here is one exception, in a quiet side street, and easily picked out by the Essex weatherboarding, unusual in this area. The pub's rich history, dating from 1731, is described in a free leaflet available at the bar, and look for the selection of ancient herbal remedies. The collection of old beer taps is appropriate for a pub with a fine reputation for hand-pulled beers, also popular for good food, fresh seafood being a speciality. Chris and Jane Warton took over in '89, and welcome well behaved children. Barbecues are lit in the large patio/garden in summer (weather permitting). Parking could be tricky, but it's an easy walk from the town centre.

THE WHITE HORSE

Rede Road, Whepstead, nr Bury St. Edmunds. Tel. (0284) 735542
  Location: Outskirts of village, off A143.
Credit cards: Not accepted.
  Bitters: Rayments, Greene King.
  Lagers: Harp, Stella Artois.

Examples of bar meals (lunch & evening, 7 days – revised daily): *steaks, Italian meatballs, Maylasian chicken, sweet'n'sour pork, mussels in cider, lamb paprika, beef & veg. curry, kebabs, fresh fish Friday & Saturday, salads, vegetarian dishes.*

Mauritian cooking dosen't often appear on the average bill of fare, but David and Rosemary Woolf do not run an average pub. Rosemary comes from Mauritius, and her authentic native style, utilising fresh produce, made her a finalist in the 1988 'Pub Caterer of the Year' award. The everchanging menu has an excitingly cosmopolitan look, but the pub itself is firmly in keeping with the best English traditions. It began as a farmhouse in the early 17th century, becoming a public house in the early 1800s when the landlords brewed their own beer. The timber beams which supported the building then still do so now, and real fires glow in the inglenooks in winter. Slightly awkward to find, being a mile or so from the village centre, but well worth it. Children are welcome in the large garden, and inside if aged over five. Now recommended by Camra guide.

THE PLOUGH

The Green, Rede, nr Bury St. Edmunds.   Tel. (028 489) 208
Location: Cul de sac, not far from church.
Credit cards: Access, Visa.
Bitters: Greene King.
Lagers: Harp, Kronenbourg.

Examples of bar meals (lunchtime every day, & evenings except Sunday): *fresh fish (speciality), steaks, curries, salads, daily specials e.g. spicy beef, lamb with red cherries, brewers braise, pork with wine & coriander.*
Examples of restaurant meals (evenings only, not Sundays. Traditional Sunday lunch): *pigeon breasts in Madeira & spinach, venison, trout, roast duck, veal in Dijon mustard & brandy, poached salmon, local game (speciality).*

Standing on the highest point in Suffolk, the Plough is looked up to in more senses than one. Its chocolate box prettiness never lapses into tweeness; the atmosphere is relaxed and unstuffy, and the home cooked food is good value and served in generous portions. Built around 1610, it occupies an exceptionally peaceful and lovely spot in a cul de sac by the village pond. One can sit here or at the back in the large sunny garden with a tropical aviary, a dovecote and ponies – children love it! They are welcome inside in the eating areas, but will probably not appreciate the superb inglenook, timber beams and fine collection of teapots. The separate restaurant has a good name, and the Plough is a regular in national guides.

THE HARE INN

High Street, Long Melford.

Tel. (0787) 310379

Location: On the main road north of village, opp. Kentwell Hall.
Credit cards: Access, Visa.
Bitters: Greene King Abbot & IPA.
Lagers: Kronenbourg, Harp.

Examples of bar meals (lunch & evening, 7 days): *Scotch salmon & cheese bake, mushroom & asparagus au gratin, steaks, mixed grill, grilled fish of day, scampi Newburgh, chicken princess (supreme with prawns & asparagus, finished with white wine & cream sauce), pork fillet Clementine (fillet with cointreau sauce, finished with fresh orange & cream), lasagne, veg. curry, taco flats, cottage pie, salads, sandwiches. Trad Sun roasts from £5.50 (booking advised).*

Long Melford is England's longest village, the parish church is a particularly fine (some say finest) example of its kind, and there are two stately homes (Melford Hall, Kentwell Hall) within yards of each other; all good reasons for a visit, but be sure to include The Hare in your itinerary. The facade is simple Georgian, but its Tudor origins are unmistakable inside. Imposing English oak beams span the ceiling and an open fire crackles invitingly, tables and chairs nestled snugly around it. John and Jill Pipe have presided for 11 years. They take special pride in their prime home produced Suffolk beef, and east coast fish dishes are another speciality. Free seafood snacks are on the bar Sunday lunchtimes. Recommended by Egon Ronay. To the rear is a pleasant walled garden and parking. Family dining room.

THE AFFLECK ARMS

Dalham, nr Newmarket   Tel. (0638) 500306
Location: Village centre, 4¹/₂ miles south-east of Newmarket.
Credit Cards: Not accepted.
Bitters: Greene King.
Lagers: Harp, Kronenbourg.

Examples of bar meals (lunch & evening, 7 days): *homemade soups, steaks, chicken Kiev, homemade steak & kidney pie, grilled cod or plaice, seafood platter, omelettes, salads, daily specials. Sorbettes, raspberry special. Trad. Sun. roasts.*

80% of the houses in Dalham have a thatched roof – the highest rate anywhere in the country. If in Devon, say, it would be a tourist trap, but the genius of East Anglia is that it knows how to keep quiet about its many little treasures. Such a delightful village would not be complete without its old country pub, and this Elizabethan inn fulfills the role admirably. It's lovely to look at and seems to engender a remarkable atmosphere. Flowers on each table are a nice touch, and one can eat in any of three dining rooms. Children are welcome, and would enjoy the front garden which has a pleasant river frontage. Barbara Markham has been running her "simple village pub" since May '88, and maintained its place in major guides.

THE CHERRY TREE

Bury Road, Stradishall.   Tel. (0440) 820215
  Location: On A143 Bury to Haverhill road.
  Credit cards: Mastercard (only for bills over £10).
  Bitters: Greene King Abbott & IPA.
  Lagers: Harp; Kronenbourg.

Examples from lunch menu (every day): *chicken sate with spicy peanut sauce, beef curry, toad in the hole, steaks, lasagne, macaroni cheese, French sticks, jacket potatoes, ploughman's, sandwiches. Trad Sun roasts £4.75 main course (booking advised).*
Examples from evening menu (every day): *beef Guinness & mushroom pie, gratin of smoked haddock with prawns, minted lamb in red wine, poached wild salmon, trio of lamb cutlets, mixed grill, steaks, vegetarian.*

One of the joys of exploring our lovely countryside is the occasional chancing upon a quite delightful little country pub. Here in the heart of rural Suffolk is one such. Set in three very pleasant acres, including a large fish pond (complete with resident ducks), this 16th century farmhouse became a pub only in 1943, taking the place of another which unfortunately was in the way of pilots taking off from RAF Stradishall! Since then there have been only four landlords, the latest being local people, Jane and Roger Marjoram, with 20 years experience in the trade. Their menus are a commendable blend of staple English favourites with a little foreign zest. Separate dining room. Children welcome in garden.

THE PLOUGH INN

Hundon, nr Clare. Tel. (0440) 86789

Location: Between Hundon and Kedington, off A143.
Credit cards: Access, Visa.
Accommodation: 8 rooms, all en suite. Caravan Club certified location.
Bitters: Nethergate, Greene King, guest.
Lagers: Carlsberg, Kronenbourg.

Examples of bar meals (lunch & evening from 6pm, 7 days): *trout & watercress pate, homemade soups, steak & kidney pie, fresh fish, steaks, ploughmans.*
Examples of restaurant meals (as above): *lemon sole with prawns, duckling breast with orange, steaks, salmon poached in wine & cream, vegetarian dishes, seafood night every Tuesday Trad. Sun. roasts (booking advised).*

It makes an eyecatching front cover, and some of the finest views in Suffolk are commanded from this elevated position, high over rolling countryside. For over 30 years The Plough has been in the hands of the Rowlinson family. Over the last nine David and Marion have carried out extensive but careful alterations to create a traditional country pub atmosphere, using soft red bricks and oak beams from an old barn. A year or two ago they added a new extension of eight en suite bedrooms, and whilst providing modern amenities (the restaurant is air conditioned, for example) have not sacrificed old fashioned friendliness and charm. This and good home cooked food has won a place in local affections and a number of major guides. Not an easy one to find, but patience reaps its rewards. Children welcome.

THE BELL INN

St. James Street, Castle Hedingham.   Tel. (0787) 60350

Location:	Village centre.
Credit cards:	Not accepted.
Accommodation:	One self-catering cottage (sleeps 3), £25 per night, £50 per weekend, £150 per week.
Bitters:	Greene King Abbot & IPA, Rayments (gravity fed from barrel).
Lagers:	Heineken, Kronenbourg.

Examples of bar meals (lunch & evening, except Monday evenings): *steak & Guinness pie, shepherds pie, lasagne, smoked prawns with garlic dip, haddock & prawn gratinee, grilled trout, sirloin steaks, spicy lamb hotpot, burgers, ploughmans. Homemade treacle tart with toffee ice cream, truffle tort.*

The beautiful hamlet of Castle Hedingham is a suitable setting for this notable 15th century inn. Previously having served as a magistrates court and a theatre, The Bell is second only to the castle itself in what was historically an important village. Solid oak beams, authentic brickwork and exposed wooden floorboards together create a medieval air, whilst the fresh flowers, real ale from the barrel and friendly service are all part of the charm for which the delightful old inn is renowned. Children are welcome in two of the spacious bars and ofcourse in the lovely walled orchard garden (with croquet). Above the saloon bar is a great hall with a superbly restored barrel ceiling, available for private hire. Live jazz (entry free) is held here on the last Sunday lunchtime of each month. Large car park to the rear.

THE GREEN MAN

Gosfield, nr Halstead. Tel. (0787) 472746
    Location: On Braintree to Hedingham road.
    Credit Cards: Access, Visa.
    Bitters: Greene King.
    Lagers: Kronenbourg.

Examples of bar meals (lunchtime 7 days, every evening except Sunday): *Evenings: game soup with sherry, breaded mushrooms with garlic butter, Dover sole, oxtail ragout, steaks, boiled beef & carrots, roast duck with orange sauce, plaice fillets with prawn sauce, steak & kidney pudding, vegetarian (e.g.spinach pancakes, vegetable lasagne).* Lunchtime: *Cold buffet, hot dish of the day.*

Not East Anglia's most attractive pub from the outside but, as with people, appearance can be misleading. Venture inside and you will find yourself in a 16th century oak beamed bar or dining area of considerable character. However, your eyes will be drawn immediately to the splendid buffet table, which looks ready to collapse under the weight of massive king prawns, fresh salmon, succulent roasts and more. This is supplemented at lunchtime by a hot dish of the day, and all is home cooked. Special requests are catered for, if possible, and bookings accepted. There's also a small function room for private parties. Children are tolerated if well behaved; if not, there's a rather nice garden by the large car park. Proprietor John Arnold can be proud of his successful well-run business, but modestly claims that colleague Janet Harrington, who supervises daily affairs, is the driving force behind it.

THE ROSE AND CROWN

Nayland Road, Gt Horkesley, nr Colchester.   Tel. (0206) 271251
Location: On A134 Colchester to Sudbury Road.
Credit cards: Access, Visa.
Bitters: Greene King.
Lagers: Harp, Kronenbourg.

Examples of bar meals (lunch & evening, 7 days): *moules mariniere, Suffolk hotpot, game, steaks, fresh fish & seafood, ploughman's, sandwiches.*
Examples of restaurant meals (every evening, plus trad. Sun. roast): *spicy Cajun prawns, crispy coated vegetables with dip, beefsteak kidney & mushroom pie with Guinness, seafood pie, Indian style chicken, kleftico, pork & mustard sausages, homemade burgers, steaks, poached salmon with tarragon sauce, trout stuffed with prawns & mushrooms, brown rice & hazelnut roast with redcurrant sauce, red bean creole, salads.*

A common name for a pub that is anything but: a huge and diverse menu, as appetising as it is imaginative, places this Rose and Crown amongst the aristocracy. As the photo shows, it also happens to be quite a handsome building, dating from around 1700, and is replete with exposed timbers and brickwork, open woodburner, rustic style furniture and various equine artefacts. The intimate 46-seater restaurant, formerly the wine cellar, is the scene of theme evenings, held throughout the year, a chance for the chef Martin Duggan to show the range of his talents. Phil and Sue Hirst have been licensees since summer 1990, and their welcome extends to children. Barbecues are lit in the garden in season. Large car park.

THE CHEQUERS

The Square, Goldhanger, nr Maldon.   Tel. (0621) 88203

Location:	Village square, next to church.
Credit cards:	Not accepted.
Accommodation:	3 twin rooms.
	Car park & beer garden. Coaches welcome.
Bitters:	Courage Best & Directors, Greene King, Tolly Cobbold.
Lagers:	Hofmeister, Fosters, Kronenbourg.

Examples from extensive bar menu (lunch & evening, 7 days): *ploughman lunches, basket meals, shepherds pie, lasagne, sandwiches, salads.*
In the separate restaurant (evenings only, 7 days in summer.): *fine selection of fish, fowl & steak dishes, all accompanied by fresh seasonal vegetables.*

The Chequers Inn began life in 1410 as a courthouse, where unfortunates were undoubtedly tried, sentenced, probably executed in the square, and buried in the adjacent churchyard. Most likely some smugglers of the time would have trod the same steps, considering that the inn is just five minutes walk from the River Blackwater. The more exalted Prince Nicholas of Russia had a rather happier time on his stay at The Chequers. There's no hint now of the morbid past, but the medieval character of the building is still evident, and remains unaltered, with its old taproom, festooned with rods, traps, and guns; the snug bar, family room and the intimate and ornamental restaurant located off the saloon bar – the latter yielding to the irreverent strains of jazz every other Sunday, and piano on Saturday evenings. Trevor and Joan Jones are always delighted to welcome allcomers, including children.

THE JOLLY SAILOR

Church Street, Hythe Quay, Maldon.   Tel. (0621) 853463

Location:	Quayside, bottom of Church Street.
Credit Cards:	Visa.
Accommodation:	1 double, 2 twins, 1 family.
Bitters:	Adnams, Ruddles, Websters, Trumans mild.
Lagers:	Holsten, Fosters, Carlsberg.

Examples of bar meals (available all opening hours): *ploughmans, sandwiches, daily specials e.g. fresh prawn salad, plaice, cod, sausage, French bread specials, vegetarain dishes. Evenings only: basket meals, pizzas (specify toppings), steak meals.*

The Jolly Sailor is described by the D.O.E. as a "16th century timber framed house with 18th century plastered front. Commenced as public house in 1874". Such dry prose does not do justice to a fine quayside inn. Transforms from sailing barges are mounted on plaques forming a most attractive and unusual theme to the decor. Navigation lights from ships provide illumination to match, and the bar has the traditional oak beams. If you like a taste of the briney air with your drink, repair to the large attractive garden and patio overlooking the quay, and be serenaded by birdsong from the aviary. Lovely Maldon park and the town itself are close at hand, and as parking at the Jolly Sailor is limited this may be the best way to plan your visit. The food is simple but wholesome, and very reasonably priced. In summer, Gordon and Phil Bell lay on a barbecue to which children are also welcome. Incidentally, the pub is due to be featured in the tv series 'Lovejoy'.

THE HURDLE MAKERS ARMS

Post Office Road, Woodham Mortimer, nr Maldon.   Tel. (024 541) 5169
Location: Between A414 and B1010.
Credit cards: Not accepted.
Bitters: Greene King.
Lagers: Heineken, Tennents Extra.

Examples of bar meals (lunchtimes only, 7 days): *lasagne, grilled gammon, ham off the bone, homemade steak kidney & mushroom pie, Mediterranean prawn salad, various fillings in rolls & sandwiches, ploughmans, Devon smoked prawns, curries, smoked chicken, grilled lemon sole. Homemade fruit pie.*

Winner of the Camra 'Pub of the Year' (1988), The Hurdle Makers has a name and style all its own. It began life as a farmhouse, changed to an off-licence and, in 1871, finally became a pub. It is set in two acres of well tended garden, wherein is a children's play area – there's also a family room. Such a garden readily accommodates regular barbecues, at which up to 200 can sit under 'sunbrellas', or into a marquee if necessary. The menu above, though typical, changes weekly. The food is totally fresh and never fried; Terry and Sue Green take pride in that, and also advise customers that no bookings are taken, just arrive. Inside you'll find two lovely oak beamed bars with stone flagged floors, settles dotted round tables and an open fire. All the washrooms are immaculate, and the disabled have their own. Pub bar has darts, dominoes and shut-the-box.

THE DUKE OF YORK

Southend Road, Billericay.   Tel. (0277) 651403

         Location: On A129 to Wickford (old Southend Road), 1 mile from town.
    Credit cards: Access, Visa, Amex, Diners.
          Bitters: Greene King Abbot & IPA, McEwans, Toby.
           Lagers: Heineken, Tennents, Tennents Extra, Tennents LA,
                  Kronenbourg.

Examples of bar meals (lunch & evening every day except Saturday evening and all day Sunday): *homemade soups & pies, salads, jacket potatoes with various fillings, steaks, curries, sandwiches, many daily specials eg spaghetti with prawns peppers & cream, bubble & squeak, pork chops Swiss style.*

Examples of restaurant meals (as above): *scallops mornay, steaks, Dover sole meuniere, veal georgette, large vegetarian menu (vegans catered for), many daily specials eg strips of chicken in potted shrimp sauce, monkfish in mussel & smoked salmon sauce, beef Wellington in red wine sauce.*

The Duke of York began life as two cottages (circa 1800), later in 1868 it became a beer house and in 1975 an extension in the form of a restaurant was added. The enthusiastic chef cooks to order from an enormous menu (in French and German also), yet achieves the distinction of a quality restaurant (expect to pay around £25 per head for a full meal) alongside a good pub at more everyday prices. Proprietor Mrs. Edna White dare not change things too much and risk incurring the displeasure of 'Swanee' – ghost in residence. Other spirits include over 50 malt whiskies, and the wine list has some real classics alongside the more modest. Children are permitted in the restaurant and everyone can bask on the small patio. Look for the antique cash till, in £ s d! Large car park.

THE ALMA ARMS

Horseman Side, Navestock Side, Brentwood.   Tel. (0277) 372629
        Location: 3 miles off Brentwood/Ongar Road.
    Credit Cards: Not accepted.
        Bitters: Adnams, Greene King, Mauldons, Ridleys, Rayments.
        Lagers: Kronenbourg, Harp, Carlsberg.

Examples of bar meals (12 noon – 2 p.m. 7.00–8:45pm, 7 days): *homemade pies (eg steak, lasagne, shepherds, chicken), fresh daily fish (eg salmon, trout, lemon sole), seafood lasagne. Homeade desserts (eg cheesecake, sherry trifle, fruit crumbles, bread & butter pudding). Daily 3 course meal £5.25. Trad. Sun. roasts (incl. dessert) £6.75.*

The Alma Arms is close to Brentwood and Harold Hill (A128) and the drive, once off the main road, through the Essex countryside is very pleasant, though not straightforward. Alan and Jane have run this busy rural inn for over 20 years, providing a varied homemade menu with the accent on value and freshness, complemented by a good range of ales. Please note the menu is extended on a Saturday night. The inn was built in 1731 but only bore the 'Alma' title since the Crimean War battle of that name. The attractive bars are oak beamed – the bar itself being brick with timber reliefs, the theme being continued to the fireplaces. A new addition is the very pleasant 40-seater Victorian conservatory, but for really warm days there is a patio to the front. Mentioned in several national guides. Large car park.

THE BLACK BULL

Dunmow Road, Fyfield, nr Ongar.   Tel. (0277 899) 225

Location:	On B184 Ongar to Dunmow road.	
Credit cards:	Access, Visa.	
Bitters:	Wadworth 6X, Courage Best & Directors.	
Lagers:	Fosters, Muller, Kronenbourg.	

Examples of bar meals (lunch & evening, 7 days): *flaked smoked haddock in cheese & wine sauce, field mushrooms in garlic butter, guacamole, Mediterranean prawns, chicken tikka with pitta bread, steaks. Fish night on Thursdays.*
Lunchtime only: *steak & kidney pie, chilli, jacket potatoes, variety of ploughmans, sandwiches.*

Now a freehouse, The Black Bull is widely regarded as being one of the best pubs for food in these parts. Proprietor Alan Smith has achieved this status by taking great pains to preserving high standards – deep frying is frowned on, and the menus are highly original, even exotic, and prepared with skill. Wild field mushrooms and a chilli that "takes no prisoners" are hardly typical pub fare. Fish lovers should be sure not to miss Thursday nights. It seems to have paid off, for the three bars always seem to be doing a good trade (indeed, an extension seating 28 has just been added), and the large car park is a neccessity. The building is 600 years old – not immediately evident, but the atmosphere is always hospitable, the staff friendly and courteous. Children welcome in gardens.

THE COCK & BELL

The Street, High Easter, Nr. Chelmsford.   Tel & Fax. (0245) 31296
      Location: Village Centre.
   Credit Cards: Access, Visa, Diners, Eurocheque.
        Bitters: Mauldens, Squires, Sheperd Neame Spitfire, Masterbrew,
                  Bishop's Finger, Thomas Hardy.
        Lagers: Cock & Bell special Swiss lager, Holsten.

Examples of bar meals (lunch & evening, 7 days): *homecooked Tudor pie, lasagne, tagliatelle, bolognese, fresh poached salmon, ploughmans, sandwiches, quiche, honeyroast homecooked ham, childrens menu.*
Example of restaurant meals (lunch & evening, except Monday evening): *traditional Sunday roast, eggs caviar, cockade – supreme of chicken poached in white wine & herbs with a creamy stilton & brandy sauce (award winner!), salmon steak poached in white wine & grenadine. Homemade scrumpy apple turnover & ice cream, waffles.*

Recipient of various national food awards for the last five years, Barrie and Bridget Day's starred listed 14th century pub is clearly exceptional. Waitresses attired as wenches serve in an upper tier dining area – booking advised as understandably it's popular. A rather special facility is a classic Rolls Royce which will transport you to and from your champagne meal. Barrie, an ex-paratrooper, is proud of the exhibition of militaria in the bar, and the armoured car in the car park which has now been joined by a jeep. Ladies may powder noses in the air raid shelter! Seekers of the curious may be intrigued by an old seed fiddle in the lounge. This lounge was once a yard through which horses were led to the well at the rear.

THE QUEEN VICTORIA

79 Stortford Road, Gt Dunmow.   Tel. (0371) 873330
Location: Just off roundabout on Dunmow by-pass.
Credit cards: Access, Visa.
Bitters: Mauldon Squires, Greene King, Brewers.
Lagers: Fosters, Kronenbourg.

Examples of bar meals (lunch & evening, 7 days): *daily fresh fish, homemade pies, grills, salads, sandwiches.*
Examples of restaurant meals (lunch & evening, 6 days. Trad. Sun. lunch): *homemade soup, platter of prawns, poached salmon & cucumber sauce, scampi provencale, chicken Kiev, lamb steak with mint & honey sauce, fillet steak au poivre, steak Diane.*

We've all had the vexing experience of arriving ravenous at a pub at 1:35pm, only to be told that serving food stopped at 1:30pm. No such nonsense here; homecooked food is available as long as it's open, although the restaurant is sometimes reserved for private functions. But there are plenty of places to eat – a large bar full of nooks and crannies, and a garden with sturdy tables and chairs. Built in 1553 as three farmworkers' cottages, it is as engaging inside as the thatched exterior would suggest, and wants not for original beams, brickwork and fireplaces etc. Upholstery is in rich velour. If you like live entertainment then Friday night is yours, and barbecues are held weather permitting. Dogs and children allowed, but no special facilities. Large car park.

THE BUTCHER'S ARMS

Dunmow Road, North End, Gt Dunmow.   Tel. (0245) 37481
       Location: On A130.
   Credit cards: Not accepted.
        Bitters: Adnams, Ridley's IPA & Export.
         Lagers: Fosters, Holsten, Carlsberg Export.

Examples of bar meals (lunch & evening, 7 days): *steaks, chicken Kiev, scampi, haddock, lasagne verdi, chef's grill, spinach & mushroom lasagne, vegetable chilli, ploughman's, huffers, sandwiches, daily specials. Apple & sultana sponge, spotted dick, chocolate icecream bomb. Children's meals. Trad. Sun. roasts from Oct. – Easter (booking advised).*

Monks from nearby Black Chapel built this as their 'local' back in 1459, and vistors were accommodated here. They did their work well, for the ancient oak beams are still bearing up, and look good for another 500 years. Newcomers Mark and Jo Cracknell have quickly established a cordial atmosphere and a reputation for good, straightforward food, very reasonably priced. Bookings are taken for tables in bar or restaurant area. Families are especially welcome (the pub features in 'Let's Go' guide), and youngsters will love the menagerie in the large garden, as well as swings and climbing frame. The adjacent one-acre meadow is available for use by registered caravan clubs, or indeed any society seeking an outdoor venue.

THE GREEN DRAGON

Upper London Road, Young's End, nr Braintree. Tel. (0245) 361030
  Location: A131 2 miles south of Braintree – nr Essex showground.
  Credit cards: Visa, Mastercard, Luncheon vouchers.
  Bitters: Greene King Abbott, L.A. bottled selection.
  Lagers: Harp, Kronenbourg.

Examples of bar meals (lunch & evening, 7 days): *homemade pies, Scotch salmon, trout, mussels, lasagne, salads, Indian style chicken, fresh crab, daily blackboard specials, vegetarian dishes.*
Examples of seasonal restaurant meals (as above): *spicy Cajun prawns, fresh crab & lobster, selection of steaks, escalope of veal 'Dijon', Barbary duck, venison, chicken Napoli, exotic fruit & vegetable curry, chestnut loaf & cranberry sauce. Revised regularly, and theme evenings include Greek, Beaujolais, Elizabethan etc.*

Catering awards and accolades are routinely visited upon The Green Dragon, to the credit of Bob and Mandy Greybrook. But the pub has been one of the best liked in the area for many years. The restaurant, which seats 46, was once the old stable block but is now ingeniously converted, even retaining the old hayrack in the hayloft above. The old horse trough remains but only plants drink from it nowadays. The 'snug' really is snug and seats 12. Business or private parties can be catered for. Summer sees the barbecue glowing in the garden, where there's a play area with shop and aviary, and children are welcome. Large car park.

THE RETREAT

Bocking Church Street, Braintree.   Tel. (0376) 47947

Location:	Just off A131 Halstead Road, opposite 11th century church.
Credit cards:	Access, Visa, Amex, Diners.
Accommodation:	Three twin rooms all en suite.
Bitters:	Adnams, Ruddles, Websters, Draught Guinness.
Lagers:	Carlsberg, Holsten, Fosters.

Examples of bar meals (lunch & evening, 7 days): *scallops with cream & cheese sauce, Yorkshire pudding filled with ham onion cheese & cream sauce, courgettes filled with onion tomato & garlic topped with melted cheese.*

Examples of restaurant meals (lunchtime every day except Saturday, & evenings except Sunday. Open for Sunday lunch until 4pm): *saute medallions of venison, steaks, vegetarian dishes, lobster thermidor, duck breast with Grand Marnier sauce, chicken breast with garlic ginger & yoghurt sauce.*

The aptly named Retreat is a picturesque 15th century inn not far, but far enough, from the bustle that is Braintree. David & Margaret Locke have made changes in recent years: the restaurant is now a bar area with consequent increase in space. A new conservatory joins two converted rooms making a restaurant seating up to 50, ideal for functions, business and those just seeking a meal that is imaginative and of high quality – Egon Ronay recommended. The large sheltered garden is nicely landscaped and enclosed for those with children of an adventurous nature, who will want to peer down the ancient 30ft well in one of the bars. There is a no-smoking area and a car park.

THE WHITE HART

Thaxted Road, Wimbish, nr Saffron Walden.   Tel. (0799) 599203
    Location: On Thaxted – Saffron Walden road.
Credit cards: Not accepted.
     Bitters: Greene King IPA, Tetleys. Plus draught Guinness.
     Lagers: Castlemaine, Skol.

Examples of bar/dining room meals (lunchtime 7 days,evenings Tues – Sat):
*homemade steak & kidney pie, lasagne, quiche, gammon steak, scampi, shepherds pie,
chilli, jacket potatoes, sandwiches, blackboard specials. Children's menu.*

A good, unpretentious country pub, this, that sets out not to try to compete with
restaurants, but to provide simple yet wholesome homecooked food in the best
traditions. It's a grade II listed building, set in two acres of ground including a
sizeable car park. Inside is quite small and cosy, with a brick chimney segregating
the open plan through bar, and an 18 seater dining room, where children are
welcome. A convivial atmosphere is cultivated by Richard and Pauline Wilkins and
staff, especially evident on monthly music nights. Occasional barbecues are also
good fun. Combine your visit with a look at famous Audley End House, just five
miles away, or Mole Hall wildlife centre, also close by. Fast developing Stansted
Airport is not far, either.

THE CROWN

Little Walden, nr Saffron Walden.   Tel. (0799) 522475

Location: 1¹/₂ miles north of Saffron Walden.
Credit cards: Access, Visa, Mastercard, Eurocard.
Bitters: Boddingtons, Flowers, everchanging guests.
Lagers: Stella Artois, Heineken. Good range of bottles.

Examples of bar meals (lunch & evening, except Sun. evening): *baked mackerel, kidneys turbigo, steak & kidney pie, steaks, chilli, jugged hare with buttered noodles, liver & bacon, escalope of pork cordon bleu, curry, smoked seafood platter, whole plaice, wild mushroom stroganoff, jacket potatoes, daily specials eg skate, mussels in garlic, seafood quiche. Menu revised daily. Trad. Sun. roasts.*

National winner of Egon Ronay's "Pub of the Year" in the recent past, this is obviously no ordinary establishment. The stimulating menu, blending the new and traditional (from the kitchen of German chef, Klaus Nieland), is chalked daily on a blackboard. Likewise, the bitters are changed regularly, and mostly served straight from the barrel. Unchanging, however, is the building itself, once two 18th century cottages, although the low doors, walk-through fireplaces and timber lattices suggest much older origins, especially in the 'snug' (children welcome). Flooring ranges from terra cotta to stripped wood via luxury pile carpet, furniture is solid wood and there's a fine old grandfather clock in one corner. Steve and Sue are a friendly young couple who came here only in summer '91, and after a successful New Year party plan to celebrate other red letter days like Valentine, Halloween etc.

THE CRICKETERS ARMS

Rickling Green and Quendon, nr Saffron Walden.   Tel. (0799 88) 322
                                                 Fax (0799 88) 512

Location:	Village green, 10 mins. from Stansted Airport (courtesy car available).
Credit cards:	Access, Amex, Visa.
Accommodation:	7 rooms all en suite.
Bitters:	Tolly Original, Bateman's XXXB, monthly guest.
Lagers:	Hansa, Labatts Strong, Tennents LA.

Examples of bar meals (lunch & evening, 7 days): *grills, steak & kidney pie, haddock provencale, fresh mussels, vegetable stroganoff, salads, many dishes of the day.*
Examples of restaurant meals (as above): *moules mariniere, brace of quail, salmon Josephine (in puff pastry), duck breast in kirsch and cherry sauce. Traditional Sunday lunch 12:30 and 3:00pm sittings.*

Essex County Cricket team plays here one Friday every June. It's a good wicket and there can be few prettier village greens, but more important is the quality of refreshment available. Jo and Tim Proctor, with talented chef David, are naturally proud of their speedy recognition by major guides. Their ever growing local following is kept informed by a quarterly 'fixtures list' which will be sent on request. Look out for 'theme weeks' (e.g.French), and Wednesday is fish and chip supper night. Thursday is 'trial night', a chance to test David's ideas at just £9.95 for three courses. All is fresh and cooked to order – frozen mediocrities are taboo! Functions up to 70 can be accommodated inside, and there's also a family room. On Sundays enjoy a 'no rush' lunch, or afternoon tea on the patio listening to leather on willow.

THE AXE AND COMPASSES.

Arkesden, nr Saffron Walden.   Tel. (0799) 550272
    Location: Village centre.
    Credit cards: Access, Visa.
    Bitters: Greene King IPA & Abbot, Rayments Special.
    Lagers: Kronenbourg, Harp.

Examples of bar/restaurant meals (lunch & evening, except Mon evening): *hot seafood or vegetable broth with garlic bread, grilled dates wrapped in bacon on mild mustard cream sauce, game & Abbot ale pie, poached supreme of chicken stuffed with cream cheese & herbs in stilton & port wine sauce, fresh local trout in honey-cured bacon, fillet steak, veg. stir-fry with Chinese spices, sandwiches. Sticky toffee pudding with butterscotch sauce, boozy bananas flamed in rum, raspberry & almond pavlova. Trad. Sun. roasts.*

Newcomers to Arkesden wonder why they've never heard of it before. It is, quite simply, exquisite, and puts many a more famous place to shame. Grand old thatched houses straddle a little stream in the dappled shade of willow trees. For complete perfection a lovely old country pub is required, and that's what you have in 'The Axe and Compasses' – a picturebook 17th century house, presided over by new owner Robin Moore (also of The Anchor, Sutton Gault), aided by chef managers Robert Morley and Mirielle Ferguson. Their menus, changed monthly, indicate considerable innovation and style, alongside time-honoured favourites such as rack of lamb or roast Norfolk turkey, complemented by daily specials at lunchtime. Star rating in national good pub guide. Children welcome in restaurant and patio areas.

The Axe and Compasses, Arkesden.

THE YEW TREE INN

36 The Street, Manuden, nr Bishops Stortford. Tel. (0279) 812888

Location: 10 mins from Stansted Airport.
Credit cards: Access, Visa, Eurocard.
Accommodation: 1 single, 4 doubles, 1 family, all en suite.
Bitters: Flowers IPA, Greene King Abbot.
Lagers: Stella Artois, Heineken, Heineken Export.

Examples of bar meals (lunch & evening, except Sun. evening): *homemade steak & kidney pie, chilli, lasagne, chicken & mushroom pie, steaks, scampi, plaice, cod, rock, skate, salads, ploughman's, sandwiches, daily specials eg Somerset pork, curries.*
Examples of restaurant meals (every evening except Sun.): *trout with almonds, steaks, mixed grill, Barnsley lamb chop, moussaka, chicken in lemon sauce, beef stroganoff.*

The Yew Tree and Manuden have been acquainted for 550 years, and together represent the best of English traditions. A very pretty village in one of the most unspoilt corners of Essex, yet not far from Stansted Airport, it makes an ideal base for an overnight stay (bedrooms are well appointed). The many period features are further beautified by lovely floral displays, at which landlady Jacqui Kinnison excels. Also worth a special note is the exceptionally well kept IPA, which drinks 'like wine'. A recent addition is a super new restaurant, carefully constructed from ships' timbers to blend with the established building. English, continental and vegetarian cuisine, with stress on freshness, enjoys a fine reputation. Functions of all kinds are catered for, but the romantic atmosphere lends itself to wedding receptions, a speciality.

THE WHITE HART

High Street, Puckeridge, nr Ware.   Tel. (0920) 821309
    Location: Junction of A10 with A120.
  Credit cards: Access, Visa, Diners.
      Bitters: McMullens Country, AK, Courage Directors, Abbot.
       Lagers: Stella Artois, Fosters, Steingold.

Examples of bar/restaurant meals (lunch & evening, 7 days): *hot Arbroath smokie with cheese, rollmop herring stuffed with prawns, pastrami, chicken sate with peanut butter sauce, steaks, homemade turkey & mushroom pie, moussaka, lasagne, lobster, poached halibut steak with seafood sauce, large vegetarian menu, daily roast, ploughman's, sandwiches. Children's menu. Senior citizen's special lunch £3 (3 courses + coffee) every Thursday.*

Will you take up the 'seafood platter salad challenge'? If you can completely consume (unaided) a huge plateful of cold seafood with salad, you will be presented with a voucher for £6.95 to be deducted from your next meal. It's a bold offer from affable hosts Colin and Rita Boom, who've been here 11 years, and whose speciality is seafood. But there's much else to commend at this celebrated lovely old Tudor pub, runner-up in the national Guinness pub food award, rated by good food guides and the Vegetarian Society Handbook. Colin follows in the distinguished footsteps of Henry VIII and the Duke of Wellington in acquiring the manorship of Standon Rectory, mentioned in Domesday. Over 5's are welcome, and will thrill to the Shetland ponies, sheep, ducks, rabbits etc, and swings in the garden. Ask about the odd tale of 'the lady up the chimney'.

THE FOX & HOUNDS

High Street, Hunsdon.   Tel. (0279) 842369
 - Location: Village centre.
 - Credit cards: Access, Visa, Mastercard, Eurocard.
 - Bitters: Greene King Abbot & IPA, Rayments.
 - Lagers: Stella Artois, Kronenbourg, Harp.

Examples of bar meals (lunch & evening, 7 days): *mushroom & tarragon soup, chicken breast with Cumberland sauce, homemade steak & kidney pie, crispy roast duck with orange sauce, prime plaice fillet, vegetarian dishes, ploughman's, sandwiches. Menu revised daily.*
Examples of restaurant meals (as above): *avocado filled with crab & baked in rich cheese & wine sauce, rack of lamb with apricot stuffing & lamb jus, braised saddle of venison (in cognac, port & cranberries), poached sea bream with saffron sauce, sirloin steak. Trad Sun roast £9 (3 courses).*

Carl Yardley trained as a chef at London's Hilton Hotel, so expect far-above-average pub fare when you come to this peaceful, pretty little village, just minutes from Harlow. He and wife Pauline completely overhauled their attractive 17th century pub when they took over in 1990. The best of English pub traditions live on; large open fireplaces, beams and studwork, horse bits and brasses, and decor on the theme of fox, hounds and horses. Traditional celebrations are also honoured, such as Valentine and Beaujolais nights. Children are especially welcome; smaller portions are available, and there are outdoor games (including bouncy castle) and a barbecue in the garden. There are plans to hold children's outdoor parties. Dining room also available for functions.

THE GEORGE & DRAGON

High Street, Watton-at-Stone. Tel. (0920) 830285

Location: Village centre, between Stevenage & Hertford.
Credit cards: Access, Visa, Diners, Amex.
Bitters: Greene King. Plus draught Guinness & dry Blackthorn cider.
Lagers: Harp, Kronenbourg.

Examples of bar meals (lunch & evening, except Sundays): *Corsican fish soup, tomato & basil tart, 'millionaire's bun' (with fillet steak), lambs' kidneys in madeira wine, strips of pork fillet cooked in sauce (with bean shoots, ginger & spring onions), vegetarian dish, salads, sandwiches, ploughman's, dish of the day.*
Examples of restaurant meals (lunch & evening, except Sundays & Mondays): *Alsatian hot savoury onion tart, herring roes in butter & fresh lime, paupiettes of fresh sole filled with salmon mousse, chicken breast stuffed with black cherries & covered with white wine & dill sauce, steaks, pimento filled with spiced kidney bean bordelaise.*

"The pub with the club atmosphere" – that's how it's often known, the achievement over the years of Kevin and Christine Dinnin. Not only the warmth and hospitality are outstanding: the homecooked food, as a glance over the examples above will suggest, is of the first order, sufficient to secure a regular place, indeed a star rating in the main national pub guides. Occasional special nights add further interest, and the wine list is always excellent. Built as a pub in 1603, it exudes an air of comfort and well being, with its old beams, antique furniture and prints, and fresh flowers in abundance. To relax by the log fire with the papers (provided) and good food and drink is a simple pleasure not to be missed. Children welcome as far as facilities will allow, but there is a garden and patio.

THE LYTTON ARMS

Park Lane, Knebworth.   Tel. (0438) 812312

       Location: Mid-way between Knebworth & Codicote.
Credit cards: Access, Visa.
        Bitters: Shefford, Adnams, Bass, Theakstons, 6 guests.
        Lagers: Becks, Carslberg, plus imported bottled. Range of real
                ciders from the cellar.

Examples of bar meals (lunch & evening, 7 days): *stilton mushrooms, deep fried brie, steaks, mixed grill, chicken Kiev, homemade steak & mushroom pie, trout with prawns, chicken tikka, homemade lasagne, scampi, cod, quiche, salads, ploughman's, sandwiches, daily specials. Cheesecake, spotted dick, lemon meringue pie.*

Knebworth House is one of the most noteworthy stately homes in the land, and this traditional 19th century country pub is part of the Lytton family estate (old photographs of the Lyttons and Knebworth form part of the decor in the lounge bar). So the countryside in these parts is very pleasant, ideal for ramblers and cyclists, and after stretching the legs and filling the lungs you'll be ready for a good beer and wholesome home-prepared food. Both are available in good measure here (and a log fire in winter), and the wide range of 'real' ales has earned a place in the Camra guide. Proprietor Stephen Nye has been pulling pints here for about four years. There's a garden and patio (barbecues summer weekends) with play facilities for children, and large car park.

THE ROSE & CROWN

69 High Street, Ashwell, nr Baldock.　　　　　　　Tel. (0462) 742420
　　　Location:　Village centre.
　Credit cards:　Visa, Mastercard, Eurocard.
　　　Bitters:　Greene King.
　　　Lagers:　Harp, Kronenbourg.

Examples from lunchtime menu (7 days): *peppered goat's cheese on toasted French bread, Crown smokies, homebaked ham, steak & kidney pie with Abbot ale, salmon & broccoli pie, steaks, jacket potatoes, sandwiches, daily special.*
Examples from evening menu (Tues – Sat): *lemon sole fillet with orange sauce, medallions of English lamb (sauted in wine, garlic & rosemary), half pheasant in whisky sauce, seafood collage in light creamy sauce, steaks, mushroom stroganoff, vegetable au gratin, seasonal specials.*
NB *Tuesday is "fish & chip day", lunch & evening.*

We all know of pubs that have been spoiled by too much emphasis on food: one feels guilty in just asking for a drink. Whilst quality homecooked food is very important here, one may equally enjoy a relaxed, unhurried drink in an amiable atmosphere, without feeling under any obligation to eat. The bar is divided into four cosy areas, one set aside for games. Courting couples should look for the 'nooky seat'. The magnificent inglenook indicates great age, and the building is said to be haunted, not unusual in a 15th century coaching inn. Children are welcome in eating areas or in the very pleasant garden to the rear of the car park.

125

THE MAD DOG

Little Odell. Tel. (0234) 720221

Location: On Harrold to Sharnbrook road.
Credit cards: Access, Visa.
Bitters: Greene King.
Lagers: Harp, Kronenbourg.

Examples of lunchtime bar meals (7 days): *homemade steak & kidney pie, chicken & mushroom pie, chilli, cod, plaice, king rib, steakwich, sandwiches, ploughman's, jacket potatoes, daily specials, vegetarian menu eg wheat & walnut casserole, veg. curry. Apple strudel, sponge pudding, gateau.*
Examples of evening bar meals (7 days): *as above plus:– chicken breast stuffed with leeks & served in stilton sauce, scampi, curry, duck, steak, plaice stuffed with prawns & mushrooms in white wine sauce, local venison.*

"The little pub with the large menu" – a fair summary of this attractive 16th century stone and thatch hostelry. But there's much more to say about it: the odd name derives from the original landlord, who is said to have dispensed treatment for dogbites. Maybe it is one of his hapless patients who has been the cause of mysterious happenings, reported by generations of landlords, particularly in the room with the inglenook. The interesting decor includes a collection of scales, gin traps, china plates, and a rare poster with the legend "Help the war effort. Drink draught beer". Proprietors of nine years Ken and Jean Parry organise occasional midweek barbecues, and theme evenings in winter. Children are welcome in the garden where there's a special play area with an old circus roundabout, swings and Wendy House. In CAMRA good beer guide for last eight years.

THE BELL

Horsefair Lane, Odell. Tel. (0234) 720254
Location: Village centre.
Credit cards: Not acceped.
Bitters: Greene King.
Lagers: Harp, Kronenbourg.

Examples of bar meals (no cooked food on Sundays): *homemade pies (eg turkey with leek & mushroom, or pork with apple & cider, or steak & kidney), meat platters, scampi, roast chicken, gammon steak, pizzas, vegetable flan, bacon flan, sandwiches, ploughman's, blackboard specials. Torte Montmarte, cheesecake, chocolate fudge gateau, Danish pastry.*

It looks every inch the ideal thatched country pub, and for once appearances are not deceptive. Tucked away in a quiet village, not far from Odell Country Park, its 16th century origins are apparent from the superb inglenook and exposed beams in the five rather cosy bar areas. One may eat anywhere and be sure of good, home-produced food, prepared by the landlady herself, Doreen Scott (look for the blackboard specials). With husband Derek she has been at The Bell for about six years, and they have made it popular for the friendly atmosphere, (no wailing jukeboxes to disturb), as much as the good food. Children have an area set aside for them, but will be sure to head for the little river which tumbles past at the end of the garden. Not one to be missed, and rated by major national guides.

THE WHITE HORSE

Great North Road, Eaton Socon.   Tel. (0480) 74453
          Location: Village centre – Main road.
       Credit cards: Access, Visa.
     Accommodation: Three doubles.
            Bitters: Marstons, Flowers, Whitbreads, weekly guest.
             Lagers: Stella Artois, Heineken.

Exanples of bar meals (lunch & evening, 7 days): *steak pie, chicken Kiev, lasagne, chilli, steaks, cod, plaice, salads, ploughman's.*
Examples of restaurant meals (lunch & evening Tues – Sat, plus trad. Sun. lunch): *salmon roti, panfried venison in rich sauce with juniper berries, breast of chicken (with homemade stuffing) served with hazelnut liqueur sauce.*

Dickens and Pepys were but two of many to rest at this former coaching inn on the Great North Road, situated near the River Ouse. Inside, history impresses itself on the visitor. The rooms are cosy with high back settles and with a superb inglenook housing a cheering log fire. The tables are topped with warm copper and its natural counterpart, brass, shines from horse brasses and platters. New proprietors Linda and Peter Stapleford continue to offer extensive menus, accompanied by a wine list well above the norm, and the quality earns places in major national guides. A friendly lady ghost is said to visit, obviously temporarily forsaking paradise to be here. Large beer garden with children's play area.

THE HOOPS

High Street, Gt Eversden. Tel. (0223) 262185

Location: Village centre, off A603, c. 20 mins drive from Cambridge.
Credit cards: Not accepted.
Accommodation: 1 double, 3 singles, with tv & tea & coffee.
Bitters: Chas. Wells, Adnams Broadside.
Lagers: Marksman, Red Stripe, Kellerbrau.

Examples from lunch menu (not Mondays): *trawler pie, cottage pie, steak & kidney pie, chicken ham & leek pie, cheese & tomato pizza, fisherman's platter, cod, plaice, jacket potatoes, salads, daily homebaked rolls.*
Examples from evening menu (not Mondays): *venison in red wine sauce, duck a l'orange, chicken filled with leek & stilton, pork marsala, lemon sole in prawn & mushroom sauce, salmon in asparagus sauce, plaice stuffed with prawns & mushrooms. Sponge pudding, special icecreams. Monthly theme evenings.*

A friendly, unpretentious little country inn, this, which has worked its way into more than one national guide, and is fondly regarded in the area, especially by local sportsmen, whose impressive array of trophies is on display. Indoor athletes can play pool or darts in the public bar. Those with more cerebral interests should note the original tile flooring and exposed beams in the pretty little dining room, which date from 1680 and are in amazingly good condition. If you stay overnight, look for the curved timbers upstairs, taken from sailing ships. Alan and Ramus Hawkins have, over 10 years, served generous helpings of good traditional fare, supplemented by monthly "cooking round the world" theme evenings – could be anywhere from China to the Caribbean. Children welcome in large garden, dogs permitted.

THE THREE HILLS

Bartlow, nr Linton.   Tel. (0223) 891259
Location: One mile off A604 Cambridge-Haverhill Road.
Credit cards: Access, Visa, Mastercard.
Bitters: Greene King.
Lagers: Kronenbourg.

Examples of bar meals (lunch & evening, 7 days): *trout in almonds, peach glazed gammon, fine Scotch steaks, turbot, monkfish (grills & fresh fish a speciality), lamb cutlets, vegetarian. Banana tropic, black cherries with ice cream, homeade syllabub & pavlova.*
Examples of restaurant meals (evenings only except Monday, plus Sunday lunch. Other lunchtimes by reservation): *similar to bar meals but far more extensive, and may be enjoyed in comfort of dining room.*

A visit to The Three Hills will confirm that our better pubs have much to offer. Here good English fare is presented by hosts Sue and Steve Dixon, prepared with care and served generously, earning a place in most leading guides. Their attractive 15th century inn has the interior of the quintessential English pub – oak beams blending with polished brasswork and inglenooks, logs burning within when needed. Children are welcome in the restaurant and also in the very pleasant walled garden. The surrounds are idyllic, perhaps because of being somewhat off the well trodden path, and juke boxes and other agents of deafness do not spoil the tranquillity. The hills referred to are Roman burial mounds, of great interest to antiquarians. Car parking.

THE JOHN BARLEYCORN

Moorfield Road, Duxford.   Tel. (0223) 832699
      Location: Village centre.
  Credit cards: Not accepted.
       Bitters: Greene King.
        Lagers: Kronenbourg, Harp.

Examples of bar meals (lunch & evening, 7 days, except Christmas day): *smoked haddock with poached eggs, homemade salmon mousse, casseroled pigeon, lamb & vegetable pie, open salad sandwiches. Grills include sirloin, trout, gammon. Homemade sweets.*

If you wanted to show a foreign guest the ideal English country pub, then you need look no further than the John Barleycorn. The name itself belongs to ancient folklore; celebrated in song it is a kind of shorthand for the natural things that make up good ale. Find yourself a corner in the single, snug bar and sample some of the delicious and very original fare, which has earned enthusiastic reviews in national guides and local journals. Or take to the pleasant garden at the rear where a small barn has been converted to the Garden Room. Barbecues are held here, and you may arrange your own party (min. 10 people). Christmas starts on December 1st, from when an extensive special menu for private parties of eight or more is available. Book early to see in the New Year with a supper party, followed by some fancy footwork on the dance floor, perhaps!

THE LONGBOW

Church Street, Stapleford.   Tel. (0223) 844150
  Location: Just off A1301, 5 miles south of Cambridge.
  Credit cards: Not accepted.
  Bitters: Greene King IPA, Ruddles County, Courage Directors.
  Lagers: Carlsberg, Fosters, Holsten.

Examples of bar/restaurant meals (lunch & evening, except Mon & Tues evenings): *homemade fish pie, steak & kidney pie, chicken & mushroom pie, chilli, spaghetti Bolognese, steaks, scampi, plaice, omelettes, jacket potatoes, ploughman's, sandwiches. Trad. Sun. roasts £5.95 (booking advised).*

The longbow occupies a special place in English history, evoking the spirit of Agincourt, so it is not an inappropriate name for that other bastion of Englishness, the country pub. This one has stood here for over 200 years, and was formerly known as the Three Horseshoes. Chris and Denise began their stewardship only on October '91, coming from the unlikely backgrounds of horologist and ballet teacher respectively. They have acquitted themselves most capably, and have introduced fish nights on Thursday, steak nights Friday (all is homecooked) and monthly live jazz. The Christmas thrift club continues as before. A large extension houses the restaurant, and now bar billiards has been added to the darts and other indoor pursuits. Children are welcome, and have play equipment in the garden. Details of outside catering available on request.

THE ANCIENT SHEPHERDS

High Street, Fen Ditton, Cambridge.   Tel. (022 05) 3280
    Location: Off A45 on B1047 (signed Cambridge Airport).
  Credit cards: Access, Visa.
     Bitters: Tolly Cobbold, Camerons.
     Lagers: Labatt, Hansa. Plus Guinness & Stowford Press cider.

Examples of bar/restaurant meals (lunch & evenings except Sundays): *chilli, jacket potatoes, ploughman's, sandwiches, vegetarian dish, fish specials, fresh salmon with pernod & cream, steaks, steak & kidney pie, chicken 'Ancient Shepherds' (breast pan fried with apricots, served with brandy & cream sauce), pork stroganoff, Hawaiian pancake, salads, daily blackboard specials.*

The Ancient Order of Shepherders used to meet here, but its origins are in 1540, when it was three humble cottages. The three bars and separate dining room are cosy and full of character, with beams, inglenook and lots of brasses, topped by a crooked chimney! Hilton and Anne Rose took over six years ago, and have won a place in the affections of locals and national guides with their easy and friendly manner, and fresh homecooked food. Anne hails from Scotland and Hilton from New Zealand, which accounts for the antipodean oddities around the place. Bagatelle is one unusual pastime, or stretch the brain cells a little with chess or draughts, to the soothing accompaniment of soft classical music. Children (not babies) are welcome if well behaved, and there's a patio/garden (barbecues held) where dogs are permitted. Large car park.

THE RED LION

214 The Street, Kirtling, nr Newmarket.   Tel. (0638) 730162
     Location: From Newmarket take Woodditton road (opp. Heath Garage).
                Turn left in Kirtling village towards Cheveley.
 Credit cards: Not accepted.
      Bitters: Adnams. Plus draught mild.
      Lagers: Carlsberg Export, Harp.

Examples of bar/restaurant meals (lunch & evening, 7 days): *potato skins with spicy dip, steak kidney & mushroom pie, chicken Kiev, steaks & grills, king prawns, lemon sole, vegetarian chilli, lasagne, broccoli & cream cheese pie, daily specials eg salmon in wine with prawns & mushrooms. Treacle tart, fruit crumble, bread & butter pudding, fresh cream trifle. Trad Sun roasts.*

The tiny, picturesque village of Kirtling slumbers on, apparently immune to the bustle of modern life. It's only a 10 minute drive from Newmarket, and the trip will be well rewarded by a 'discovery', this delightful 17th century inn, much larger than it first appears. Scots will feel at home in the cosy bar, with its uncommon tartan carpet and fabrics. The good, homecooked food may be enjoyed here or in the rather smart restaurant. Roger and Carol Gransden (holder of Advance Hygiene Certificate) are obliging hosts; they provide access to the disabled, high chairs for toddlers, serve afternoon teas and welcome coach parties by arrangement. An old folks' lunch club meets here every Tuesday lunchtime – all are welcome. Children are also welcome, and have swings in the garden, while the grown-ups can amuse themselves wih petanque, darts or crib.

THE THREE BLACKBIRDS

Woodditton, nr Newmarket.   Tel. (0638) 730811
>   Location: Village centre.
>   Credit cards: Access, Visa.
>   Bitters: Tolly Cobbold. Plus draught Guinness & Stowford Press cider.
>   Lagers: Hansa, plus large range of bottled.

Examples of bar/restaurant meals (lunch & evening, 7 days): *stuffed mushrooms, white asparagus, calamares, seafood gratin, venison in red wine, chicken in white wine & grain mustard & cream sauce, Scotch steaks, scampi, plaice, haddock, breadcrumbed escalope of pork in provencal sauce, lasagne (noted), homecooked ham, fish specialities (noted), vegetarian dish of the day, blackboard specials. Trad. Sun. lunch.*

A huge collection of business cards (including that of a High Commissioner of New Zealand) from all over the world, pinned around the bar, is eloquent testimony to the wide renown of this thatched and beamed 17th century village pub, regularly feted by the major national guides. Credit for this must go to proprietors Joan and Ted Spooner, who came here 11 years ago from a restaurant in Spain. Being so close to Newmarket, much of the clientele is from the world of racing, including some famous faces, but the reception from both sides of the bar is always friendly, and this 'spirit' is also entered into apparently by the ghost of a victim murdered here 300 years ago! Pride is taken in the fresh, homecooked food, which may be enjoyed in the bar or either restaurant – the one upstairs is very atmospheric and ideal for a large party. Well behaved children are welcome, and the garden has a play area. Well placed for Cambridge and most parts of the region.

THE BELL INN

Kennett, nr Newmarket.   Tel. (0638) 750286
  Location: Crossroads B1506 & B1085, on old A45.
Credit cards: Access, Visa.
Accommodation: Eight twins/doubles, all en suite.
    Bitters: Adnams, Flowers, Courage, Nethergate, John Smith, guests.
    Lagers: Carlsberg, Kronenbourg, Fosters, Dansk LA.

Examples from lunch menu (7 days): *fruits de mer, fresh haddock, spaghetti, steaks, omelettes, homemade pies, ploughman's, daily specials eg whole plaice, chicken Kiev. Trad. Sun. roasts.*
Examples from evening menu (7 days): *oysters, escargots, lemon sole, salmon, rainbow trout, chicken in red wine with asparagus, pork Holstein, steaks.*

It is thought the boundary between Suffolk and Cambridgeshire runs through this substantial Tudor inn. It used to be highwaymen who ran through it to escape the law – their hiding hole in the attic is still there. Much else is preserved: the interior is graced by great oak beams and imposing brick fireplaces, recapturing some of the romance of those times. Accommodation (in an adjacent block) is right up-to-date, however, very comfortable and lacking not in modern amenity. One is ideally placed here for many of the region's major attractions: Newmarket is only a mile or two, Cambridge, Bury St Edmunds and Ipswich are all a very easy drive. Leading national guides commend the food, seafood being the speciality, although guests are invited to ask for their favourite dish if it is not on the menu.

THE CARPENTER'S ARMS

76 Brook Street, Soham.   Tel. (0353) 720869

Location:	Turn off main road opp. Cherry Tree pub.
Credit cards:	Not accepted.
Bitters:	Batemans, Marston's Pedigree, Old Speckled Hen, Everard's Tiger, Thwaites, Varsity, Wadworth 6X, Adnams, Greene King Abbot, Old Hook Norton.
Lagers:	Kronenbourg, Tennents, Carling.

Examples of bar meals (11am – 11pm Mon – Sat, 12 – 2pm Sun): *moussaka, chilli, lasagne, curry (Sats), burgers, liver & bacon, scampi, plaice, cod, haddock, salads, ploughman's, sandwiches, roast (Sats)*.

One of the best selections of choicest ales in the region makes this 18th century pub a must for all serious beer drinkers, and it is no surprise that it is recommended by CAMRA. It would also appear to be the focus of social life hereabouts: the local football team refresh themselves in the single large bar after a game (their trophies are displayed over the fireplace), an angling club meets, quiz nights and monthly live music are popular attrcations, and there are no less than three pool and five darts teams – landlord Allan Killick was himself a county player. Whatever your reason for a visit, he and wife Jenny, who took over four years ago, extend a cordial greeting, children included. The many prints of aeroplanes decorating the walls will interest some readers. Function room for up to 50. Patio under construction.

THE TRINITY FOOT

Huntingdon Road, Swavesey.   Tel. (0954) 30315
> Location: A604 Eastbound, 7 miles west of Cambridge.
> Credit cards: Access, Visa, Mastercard.
> Bitters: Flowers, Wethereds, Whitbreads.
> Lagers: Stella Artois, Heineken.

Examples of bar meals (lunchtime 7 days, every evening except Sunday): *hot garlic prawns, smoked mackerkel, omelettes, ploughmans, trout, steaks, scampi, mixed grill, beef curry, salads. Sherry trifle, meringues glace, banana split, peach melba. Seasonal daily specials eg samphire, lobster, crab, oysters.*

England boasts of only one pub named The Trinity Foot, named after a pack of beagle hounds mastered by Colonel Whitbread, whose family's beer is on sale here. The hunters eschewed the usual fox as quarry, preferring hares, sportingly giving them a chance by pursuing on foot. The Trinity part of course refers to the nearby university college. John and Brenda Mole will serve you delicious freshly prepared food in portions to satisfy the most ardent trencherman, with special evenings like French, Spanish or Potuguese to add a little zest. Well behaved children are welcome in the eating area or unleashed onto the large safe lawn. A new conservatory has just been added, and planning consent is awaited for a marquee. Despite its proximity to the A604, traffic is high up on an embamknt and is not over intrusive. Large car park. Featured in national good pub guides.

YE OLDE FERRY BOAT INN

Holywell, nr St Ives. Tel. (0480) 63227

Location: River front, Gt River Ouse.
Credit cards: Access, Visa.
Accommodation: 7 doubles, 1 twin, all with private facilities, 2 with 4-posters. From £39.99 incl.
Bitters: Adnams, Greene King, Bass, Stones, Worthington, guest.
Lagers: Carling, Tennents, Warsteiner.

Examples of bar meals (lunch & evening, 7 days): *steak & ale pie, scampi, enchilladas, chilli, various steaks, vegetarian dishes, sauteed escalope of veal, half roast duckling, pork tenderloin, salmon en croute, daily specials. Homemade desserts. Barbecues in summer, weather permitting. Special evenings – ask for list of forthcoming events.*

A contender for the title 'England's oldest inn', the 'Ferryboat' is over 1,000 years old, preceding William the Conqueror by a century. One can only be a awestruck by such staggering antiquity. Parts of the original building still stand, in particular a rare fireplace with a window in it. As one might expect, a ghost is said to walk; the sad and harmless spirit of Juliette Tewsley, who hanged herself over unrequited love a millenium ago. Her gravestone forms part of the floor near the open fireplace, and she has a lovely spot in which to spend the rest of eternity. The timbered bar commands fine views over the large garden to the river, a marvellous backdrop for a wedding reception or party. There is a function room if weather precludes. Richard and Shelley Jeffrey are the owners, Hilary Paddock the manageress.

THE ANCHOR INN

Sutton Gault, Sutton, nr Ely. Tel. (0353) 778537
Location: Off B1381, by New Bedford River.
Credit cards: Access, Visa.
Bitters: Tolly Cobbold.
Lagers: Hansa Export.

Examples of bar meals (lunch & evening every day. Please book if you have children): *gazpacho Andaluz, giant green-lipped mussels in garlic butter, curried nut loaf, tagliatelle (with blue cheese, garlic & mushrooms), chicken leek & bacon in herb crumble, steak & kidney in Guinness, rack of lamb with Cumberland sauce, fillet steak Dijonnaise, fresh panfried shark steak with prawn sauce,. Sticky toffee pudding, chocolate roulade, lemon & brandy syllabub.*

This is a real 'find', lost in the wide open spaces of the Fens. Tucked in by the river bank and surrounded by trees, it has that immediate appeal which is hard to define and even harder to simulate – for this is an authentic 350 year old ferry inn, gaslit, with panelled walls, quarry tile flooring, stripped pine furniture and open log fires. In keeping with the spirit of this remarkable pub, beer is drawn the time honoured way, straight from the barrel, and there is an unusually wide-ranging wine list. The food is of quality, original and homecooked, accompanied by freshly squeezed orange juice for drivers, perhaps. Robin and Heather Moore are your affable hosts, who permit children in one of the eating areas, though you may prefer the tables outside in the tranquil riverside setting. Recommended by other leading guides.

The Anchor Inn, Sutton Gault

141

Cambridgeshire

THE CROSS KEYS HOTEL

16 Market Hill, Chatteris.   Tel. (0354 69) 3036/2644
      Location: Main Street, opposite church.
   Credit cards: Access, Visa, Amex, Diners.
Accommodation: 7 twin/double rooms, most en suite, full facilities.
               Tourist Board 3 crowns, RAC *, AA *.
      Bitters: Greene King Abbbot, I.P.A.
      Lagers: Harp.

Examples of bar meals (lunch & evening, 7 days): *mixed grill, fresh river trout stuffed with prawns & asparagus, homemade steak pie, sandwiches, omelettes, ploughmans.*
Examples of restaurant meals (*lunchtime & evenings, 7 days*): *steaks (speciality), Nobleman's Repast, Innkeeper's Pride, Traveller's Gift, Shepherd's Delight. Table d'hote, Sunday lunch.*

Once a 16th century coaching inn, The Cross Keys retains much of its period character. The oak beamed bars are distinguished by antique clocks, rifles, and crackling log fires. The food is varied but invariably home cooking orientated, the mellow atmosphere an aid to digestion. The high standard of catering is available both on and off the premises for any private functions or small conferences. Children are welcome and are provided with a small play area in the garden. Richard and Sandra Skeggs have refurbished the bedrooms in excellent taste, with both charm and comfort in mind. One, The Cornwell Room, has a four poster and is much in demand, and the hotel would make an ideal base for those wishing to visit Cambridge, Ely, Peterborough or Kings Lynn.

142

THE BELL INN

Great North Road, Stilton.   Tel. (0733) 241066

        Location: Village centre.
    Credit cards: Access, Visa, Amex.
Accommodation: 2 singles, 14 doubles, 2 twins, 1 family, all en suite, with
                      tea & coffee, satellite tv, 2 4-posters, 5 whirlpool baths.
                      from £55 single. Special breaks £25 pp.
         Bitters: Marstons, Ruddles, tetley, Theakstons. Plus Murphy's stout.
        Lagers: Lowenbrau, Castlemaine.

Examples of bar meals (lunch & evening, 7 days): *Normandy soup, cajun prawns, steaks, beefsteak kidney & Murphy's ale pie, baguettes, stilton & plum bread.*
Examples of restaurant meals (available as above): *timbale of prawn & crab mousse wrapped in Scotch smoked salmon, thin slices of smoked duck breast with fresh basil; Byron's fillet of beef, Bell chicken supreme, lavender lamb, trio of vegetarian filo parcels. Orange & Grand Marnier pancakes.*

Stilton is ofcourse one of the world's great cheeses, and it was an 18th century landlord of the Bell, Cooper Thornhill, who first popularised it – just one chapter in the story of one of England's historic inns. Dick Turpin evaded the law here and Cromwell, Byron, Clark Gable and Joe Louis have also propped up the bar in their time. A striking building inside and out, it was, no surprise, a coaching inn, and now that the village has been bypassed the old great road is eerily quiet – good news for guests in the new accommodation (some rooms overlook the courtyard and garden). Those not so keen on a restful night's sleep should ask for the old haunted bedroom! Naturally, stilton features prominently on the menus, and the home cooking has earned distinction in various major guides. Two function rooms. Backgammon available in the Village Bar.

THE GOLDEN PHEASANT

1 Main Road, Etton.   Tel. (0733) 252387
      Location: Just off A15, between Glinton and Helpston.
  Credit cards: Access, Visa.
       Bitters: Batemans, Everards, Marstons, Greene King, Adnams, guest.
       Lagers: Kronenbourg, Harp.

Examples of bar/restaurant meals (lunch & evening, 7 days): *mussels in garlic & herb butter, local trout stuffed with almonds & prawns, salmon steak in asparagus, poached halibut, lobster thermidor (24 hrs), whole roast pheasant (24 hrs), chicken breast stuffed with prawns & lobster, steaks, lamb weeping on potatoes, mixed grill, pork slices in marsala sauce, homemade steak & kidney pie, chilli, lasagne, curry, broccoli & cream cheese pie, jacket potatoes, baguettes, sandwiches, daily specials. 3 course Trad. Sun. roasts £7.50 incl. coffee (booking advised).*

Under the new ownership of Dennis and Hilary Wilson (since December '91), formerly of The Wheatsheaf, Peterborough, this early Victorian farmhouse affords ample scope for Dennis's gardening skills (he is a previous winner of best kept garden awards). It stands in enormous grounds (the children's play area alone accounts for 1/4 acre) in a peaceful little hamlet, just a short drive from the bustle of Peterborough. Their sizeable menus, of style and originality, are supplemented by blackboard specials, but about every two months give way to theme evenings. Being one of only four pubs in the area rated by a major good beer guide, one can expect an outstanding selection of good ales, but there's also a wide choice of malt whiskies. A pleasant garden room is ideal for families.

YE OLDE WHITE HART

Main Street, Ufford.   Tel. (0780) 740250
  Location: Edge of village.
  Credit cards: Not accepted.
  Bitters: Home Brewery, Theakstons Best, Old Peculier, SB, Youngers
             Scotch and No. 3.
  Lagers: Becks, McEwans.

Examples of bar meals (lunchtime only, not Sundays or Mondays): *homemade pies, moussaka, steak & onions, fillet steak stuffed with stilton in port & herb sauce, ploughman's, sandwiches, daily specials. Children's choice. 3 course Sun. lunches (including 'beefy boats' filled Yorkshire puddings).*
Examples of a la carte (lunch & evening, except Sun. & Mon.): *'cor blimey' steak, saute of beef a la White Hart, Hooty's hearty mixed grill, jumbo prawns in garlic, veg. specials eg 'fake steak' au poivre, mushroom & asparagus hotpot, daily specials. Spotted dick, sloshed chocolate.*

On the only hill around, this 17th century inn affords a stunning panorama of the exquisite honeystone village of Ufford and beyond. In good weather, barbecues are held both at lunchtime and evening in the large garden, where children have a play area (they now also have an acre of meadow), and will love the five cats, two goats, the dog and Boris the stuffed tarantula in the bar. The interior is pretty without being twee, with a log fire and a new snug. Landlord Chris Hooton is a qualified chef and wine expert. He holds theme evenings two or three times per year, and on alternate Sunday lunchtimes there's the novelty of live jazz to accompany the roast! Live folk music may be heard every Sunday evening. Wife Sally is particularly proud of the posh ladies' room, but only half of you will be able to enjoy this. Recommended by national guides. Large car park.

Others in this series

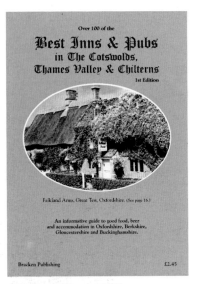

Thames Valley

Midlands

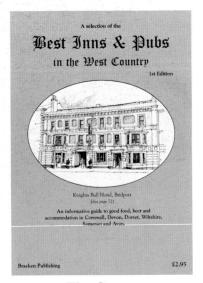

West Country

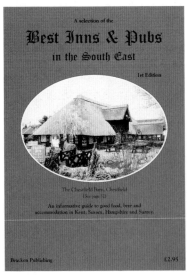

South East

Also published: Best Hotels & Restaurants in the Eastern Counties.

Available in most bookshops and some pubs within area, or by writing to Bracken Publishing, enclosing payment of £3.50 each (to include postage).

PUBLIC BARS

The bars in our friendly locals are a cherished forum for debate and free exchange of views.

But there are many countries in the world where merely expressing an opinion can put you behind bars of a quite different kind; where torture and murder of innocents are routine.

For 30 years, Amnesty International has campaigned successfully to help these brave people. Please spare a thought, and a little cash – even if only the price of a pint – while you enjoy our great English pubs in complete freedom.

Please send donations to:–

Amnesty International,
c/o Bracken Publishing,
Bracken House,
199a Holt Road, Cromer,
Norfolk NR27 9JN

THANK YOU

AMNESTY INTERNATIONAL

Notes

Index

BEDS, CAMBS & HERTS

ESSEX

* accommodation

NORFOLK

SUFFOLK

* accommodation

SUFFOLK (continued)

* accommodation

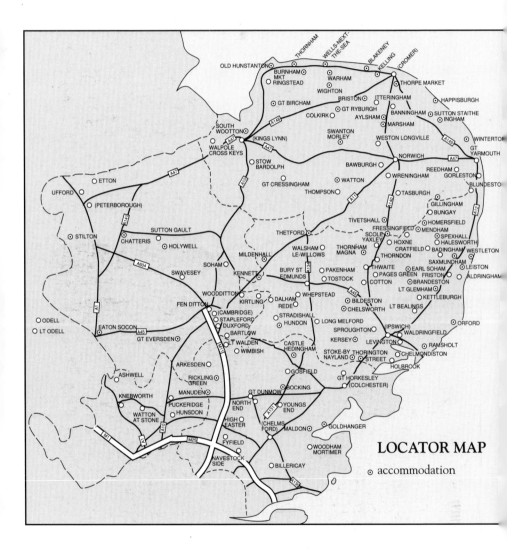

LOCATOR MAP

⊙ accommodation